Every August Bank Holiday since 1988, the Black Swan Literary Quiz in the *Sunday Times* has driven thousands of outwardly sane participants to ransack libraries, scour reference books and interrogate all conceivable sources of literary knowledge – even, in moments of desperation, pub bores and publishers – in the search for correct answers to those devilishly testing questions.

Now to celebrate Black Swan's 10th anniversary, the *Sunday Times* and Black Swan publish a compendium of literary conundrums which may justly be called the *crème de la crème*:-

THE SUNDAY TIMES/BLACK SWAN LITERARY QUIZ BOOK

This fiendishly difficult set of quizzes will have even the most knowledgeable reaching for their dictionaries of quotations and literary companions.

THE SUNDAY TIMES/ BLACK SWAN LITERARY QUIZ BOOK

Edited by Philip Evans

THE SUNDAY TIMES/BLACK SWAN
LITERARY QUIZ BOOK
A BLACK SWAN BOOK : 0 552 99563 0

First publication in Great Britain

PRINTING HISTORY
Black Swan edition published 1993

This book is set in 11/13 pt Monotype Bembo by
Phoenix Typesetting, Ilkley, West Yorkshire

Black Swan Books are published by Transworld Publishers Ltd,
61–63 Uxbridge Road, Ealing, London W5 5SA,
in Australia by Transworld Publishers (Australia) Pty Ltd,
15–25 Helles Avenue, Moorebank, NSW 2170,
and in New Zealand by Transworld Publishers (NZ) Ltd,
3 William Pickering Drive, Albany, Auckland.

Reproduced, printed and bound in Great Britain by
Cox & Wyman Ltd, Reading, Berks.

INTRODUCTION AND ACKNOWLEDGEMENTS

We have chosen eighty different topics, with questions of a ranging difficulty, and hope to have made the *Sunday Times/Black Swan Literary Quiz Book* one that's a pleasure to dip into for ten seconds or ten minutes, as well as one that will be rewarding to browse through at length.

Those who have been particularly helpful include Averil Ashfield, Meg Cairns, Vanessa Cartwright, Martina Chamberlain, Harriet Evans, Barry Forshaw, Patrick Janson-Smith, Brenda Kimber, Andrew Langley, John Latimer ('Gerry Atrix'), Andro Linklater, A.I. McIntyre a.k.a. 'Big Al', Georgina Morley, Stephen Page, Diane Pearson, Garry Perry, Paul Scherer, Andrew Schuller, Dorothy Stout, Euan Sutherland, Christopher Stobart, Pippa Turner and Judith Welsh.

CONTENTS

QUESTIONS

ACCESSORIES

'Diamonds are a girl's best friend'

LEO ROBIN

1. What do the S's stand for in a) Pearl S. Buck b) William S. Burroughs c) Dashiell S. Hammett?

2. Who is reputed to have asked, 'Is that a gun in your pocket, or are you just glad to see me?'?

3. What was contained in 'a somewhat large, black leather handbag with handles to it' left in the cloakroom at Victoria Station?

4. Who sent whom an invitation accompanied by a top hat, and the request 'Will you wear it staying with me because it is very uncommon'?

5. Who wore a sparkling cross 'which Jews might kiss and infidels adore'?

6. 'Sergeant Brown, he wears upon his shoulder
A tall green parrot as he's walking up and down
And all the parrot says is "Who's-a-pretty-boy-then?"'
What does Sergeant Brown reply?

7. Who had a beautiful blue dressing-gown without a hood?

8. Who remarked, 'Experience has taught me, when I am

shaving of a morning, to keep watch over my thoughts, because, if a line of poetry strays into my memory, my skin bristles so that the razor ceases to act'?

9. Who wrote, 'As with my hat upon my head
I walked along the Strand,
I there did meet another man
With his hat in his hand'?

10. Who suggested, 'Let us make an honourable retreat, though not with bag and baggage, yet with scrip and scrippage'?

AFFAIRS

'It's not the men in my life that count; it's the life in my men'

MAE WEST

1. In which novel does a dead dog explode on the roof where Anthony Beavis and Helen Ledidge are making love?

2. Which archbishop committed adultery on Matlock Island?

3. In which contemporary novel does Napoleon's chef fall in love with a girl with webbed feet?

4. Which novelist claimed, 'As I grow older and older,
And totter towards the tomb,
I find I care less and less
Who goes to bed with whom'?

5. Who wrote, ‘When my love swears that she is made of truth,
I do believe her, though I know she lies’?

6. In which book does someone get ‘his kiss, and it is a very large kiss indeed, with the cut-out open’?

7. In which novel appears this observation: ‘It is better somehow that a man should be unfaithful to his wife away from home’?

8. In which novel does someone remark, ‘He said it was artificial respiration but now I find I’m about to have his child’?

9. In which novel does a character complain, ‘All this fuss sleeping together. For physical pleasure I’d sooner go to my dentist’?

10. Who remarked, ‘I keep making these sex rules for myself and then I break them straight away’?

ARISTOCRATS

‘The point about the aristocracy is that they all know each other’

JILLY COOPER
Class

1. Where was heard ‘the sound of the English county families baying for broken glass’?

2. Who was Francisco Manuel da Silva?

3. What stand as proof that ‘the upper classes
have still the upper hand’?

4. Who alleged that in Boston 'The Lowells talk to the Cabots
And the Cabots talk only to God'?

5. Who said of whom that he was 'invited to all the great houses of England – once'?

6. Whose carriage awaited Jonathan Harker at the Borgo Pass?

7. Who 'by a curious fluke
Became a most important duke
From living in a vile hotel
A long way east of Camberwell'?

8. Who stated, 'I am dead: dead, but in Elysian fields'?

9. Who enthused, 'All shall equal be.
The Earl, the Marquis, and the Dook,
The Groom, the Butler, and the Cook,
The Aristocrat who banks with Coutts,
The Aristocrat who cleans the boots'?

10. Which aristocrat wrote *The Leopard*?

ART AND ARTISTS

'Painters and poets have leave to lie'

18TH-CENTURY PROVERB

1. Who wrote, 'If people knew as much about painting as I do, they wouldn't buy my pictures'?

2. Who disastrously painted his bathroom red?

3. Which 19th-century French painter declared that 'drawing is the true test of art'?

4. Who wrote that 'All Cézanne's apples I would give away
For one small Goya or a Daumier'?

5. Which novelist describes 'Resurrection' by Piero della Francesca as 'the greatest picture in the world'?

6. Who observed, 'Remember I'm an artist. You know what that means in a court of law. Next worse to an actress'?

7. Who painted scenes from the Bible, *Paradise Lost* and *The Beggar's Opera* but was better known for his satirical work?

8. Who gave a box to a prostitute with the words 'keep this for me'; and what was in the box?

9. Which 18th-century painter 'avoided the company of literary men, who were his aversion . . . and detested reading' yet wrote some most vivid and intimate letters?

10. Who wrote, 'Ah Giotto, don't prevent me from seeing Paris; and Paris, don't prevent me from seeing Giotto'?

AUTHORS

'My first meeting with Oscar Wilde was an astonishment. I never before heard a man talking with perfect sentences, as if he had written them all overnight and yet all spontaneous'

W.B. YEATS
Autobiography

1. Born in Kiev in1891, he died in 1940. Who was he and what was the title of his prose masterpiece?

2. Who wrote, 'An author who speaks about his own books is almost as bad as a mother who talks about her own children'?

3. Who is a man of history, but found his doctor's rates of exchange criminally high?

4. Who died in France on 28 January 1939 but was buried in 1949 'under bare Ben Bulben's head'?

5. Who wrote of whom and in which book that he 'wrote well but behaved rather beardsley; he made himself memorable by inventing Art, Asceticism etc, and was the leader of a set of disgusting old gentlemen called "the naughty nineties"'?

6. Of whom did Somerset Maugham opine, 'Nothing very much happens in her books, and yet, when you come to the bottom of a page, you eagerly turn it to see what happens next. Nothing very much does and again you eagerly turn the page'?

7. Who wrote, 'An author arrives at a good style when his language performs what is required of it without shyness'?

8. Who claimed, 'I am the kind of writer that people think other people are reading'?

9. Which of Dickens's novels is usually regarded as being autobiographical?

10. Who wrote *Lavengro*, and what does the word mean?

THE BARD

'Soul of an age
The applause! delight! the wonder of our stage'

BEN JONSON
'To the memory of William Shakespeare'

1. In *The Merchant of Venice* whom is the Duke addressing when he says, 'How shalt thou hope for mercy, rendering none?'?

2. Who has looks that 'are full of speed' in which play?

3. Who is fatally stabbed behind the arras?

4. Who desired 'one other gaudy night' and with whom?

5. Whose 'conscience hath a thousand several tongues'?

6. Who undertook to give

'my large kingdom for a little grave,
A little little grave, an obscure grave'?

7. Who died from a 'burning quotidian tertian' whilst babbling of green fields?

8. Who had 'on her left breast
A mole cinque-spotted'?

9. Who called for 'a plague o' these pickle herring!'?

10. Where did Sir John Falstaff lodge?

BIOGRAPHY

**'Geography is about Maps,
But biography is about Chaps'**

E.C. Bentley
Biography for Beginners

1. About whom is the biography *The Quest for Corvo*, and who wrote it?

2. Who wrote about 'Lord Lundy, who was too freely moved to tears, and thereby ruined his political career'?

3. Which famous author stated that 'a biographical account of a person is like an embalmed body with the organs and guts taken out'?

4. Name the famous novelist who wrote a vivid and engaging biography about Charlotte Brontë two years after her friend's death.

5. Who declared that 'it is by no means true that the major figures in history are the most interesting'?

6. Who stated that a biography 'simplifies even when seeking to enrich'?

7. Name the year in which one of the outstanding biographies of all time, James Boswell's *Life of Samuel Johnson*, was published.

8. Which man who came from near Malmesbury in Wiltshire was the author of a collection of lively pieces about influential people that was presented to the Ashmolean Museum in 1693?

9. Who is said to have remarked, 'I awoke one morning and found myself famous'?

10. Name the Victorians Lytton Strachey deemed eminent.

BIRTH

**'When we are born we cry that we are come
To this great stage of fools'**

WILLIAM SHAKESPEARE
King Lear

1. Who was unfortunate enough to be administered to during childbirth by Dr Slop?

2. Who was born on a Friday at twelve o'clock at night?

3. Who didn't know if they were led all that way for birth or death?

4. Who telegrammed a friend who'd just given birth, 'Congratulations. We all knew you had it in you'?

5. Which Shakespearean character proclaimed he 'was born about Three of the clock in the afternoon with a white head and something of a round belly'?

6. Which bird 'wast not born for death'?

7. Which poet warned 'You'd be bored.
Birth, and copulation, and death'?

8. Which novel describes life before birth: 'It was so snug and warm there, the feeding was automatic'?

9. Who was 'always breaking the law. He broke the law when he was born. His parents were not married'?

10. Who wrote, 'I remember, I remember,
The house where I was born,
The little window where the sun
Came peeping in at morn'?

CARICATURES AND CARTOONS

'A most unattractive old thing,
Tra la,
With a caricature of a face'

W.S. GILBERT
The Mikado

1. Whose cartoons for the tapestries for the Sistine Chapel were procured by Charles II from the Duke of Mantua?

2. Which English political caricaturist was given a pension by the Tories in 1797?

3. Which cartoonist illustrated books by Charles Dickens and Robert Surtees?

4. In addition to working for many authors the caricaturist Thomas Rowlandson formed a special link with someone who would frequently write copy to accompany Rowlandson's work. Can you name him, and their joint project?

5. Name the man who illustrated many books including *Popular Stories* by the Brothers Grimm, *John Gilpin* by William Cowper and *Robinson Crusoe* by Daniel Defoe.

6. Hogarth created the original 'Rake's Progress'. Which twentieth-century artist made a series of prints under the same title?

7. Which *Punch* illustrator was described by Whistler as 'the greatest English artist since Hogarth'?

8. Which modern artist drew the cartoons that accompanied the books by Hunter S. Thompson?

9. Which engraver published *A General History of Quadrupeds* and was famous for his endpieces?

10. Who illustrated 'the most beautifullest coat and embroidered satin waistcoat'?

CHILDREN

'Familiarity breeds contempt – and children'

MARK TWAIN
Notebooks

1. In which book do you meet Mrs Do-as-you-would-be-done-by and Mrs Be-done-by-as-you-did?

2. Who wrote, 'Better drowned than duffers if not duffers won't drown'?

3. Who was sometimes fascinated by, often scornful of, and once frightened by, the Banderlog?

4. Which gourmet picnic contained the following: cold chicken, cold ham, cold tongue . . . and had a wet ending?

5. Who dedicated a book to his stepdaughter Leonora 'without whose never-failing sympathy and encouragement this book would have been finished in half the time'?

6. Who decreed, 'Children are to be deceived with comfits, and men with oaths'?

7. Who were the Sons of Adam and the Daughters of Eve?

8. What was the unfortunate outcome of the visit to the zoo by Mr and Mrs Ramsbottom?

9. Who pointed out that 'the trouble with children is that they're not returnable'?

10. 'Speak roughly to your little boy,
    And beat him when he sneezes'
Who sang this as a lullaby? What was her baby?

CINEMA

'Cecil B. de Mille,
Rather against his will,
Was persuaded to leave Moses
Out of *The Wars of the Roses*'

E.C. BENTLEY
More Biography

1. Which novelist adapted Raymond Chandler's *The Big Sleep* and Ernest Hemingway's *To Have and Have Not* for the big screen?

2. Which actor grew a beard for a certain role 'but Metro-Goldwyn-Mayer thought it didn't look real, so I had to wear a false one'?

3. In which film did Groucho Marx observe, 'Either he's dead or my watch has stopped'?

4. Which story by Graham Greene first appeared as a screenplay for Carol Reed?

5. Which novelist-cum-film director who was found on a beach in 1975, brutally murdered, left unfinished a new novel?

6. Which director claimed that all he needed 'to make a comedy is a park, a policeman and a pretty girl'?

7. Which director remarked that 'the cinema is not a slice of life but a piece of cake'?

8. Which star cracked, 'My problem lies with reconciling my gross habits with my net income'?

9. Who said, 'If she can stand it I can. Play it!'?

10. Who stated, 'For years I have been known for saying "Include me out"; but today I am giving it up for ever'?

CRIME AND DETECTION

'It is not a fragrant world'

RAYMOND CHANDLER

1. Who was defrauded by the Eden Land Corporation of Cairo, Illinois?

2. Name the seminal American magazine in which the writings of Dashiell Hammett, Raymond Chandler and Erle Stanley Gardner first appeared.

3. What have the Givens, the Bottrells, Riddle and Tremain in common?

4. In which novel is it declared that 'almost all crime is due to the repressed desire for aesthetic expression'?

5. What was the name of Edgar Allan Poe's detective?

6. Who was the monkish detective in a medieval abbey in Shrewsbury?

7. Who described herself as 'a perfect sausage machine, a perfect sausage machine'?

8. Whose detective stories feature a Roman Catholic priest from East Anglia?

9. 'By the pricking of my thumbs
Something wicked this way comes'
Which murderer is thus heralded?

10. 'It was a robber's daughter, and her name was' – what?

DEATH

'Here lies Fred
Who was alive and is dead'

EPITAPH ON PRINCE FREDERICK – ANON

1. Who stated that 'the report of my death was an exaggeration'?

2. Of whom was it said that 'nothing in his life became him like the leaving it'?

3. Who, in a sermon, stated, 'Death is nothing at all; it does not count. I have only slipped away into the next room'?

4. Who said of whom, 'Yet she must die, else she'll betray more men'?

5. Who remarked, 'One must have a heart of stone to read the death of Little Nell without laughing'?

6. Who allowed himself to be killed by the chief of a primitive tribe as an act of expiation?

7. Who died beneath a mass of bird guano?

8. Who was shot in a leper colony?

9. What was the title of the (unfinished) novel Jane Austen was writing when she died?

10. To whom does this refer? 'It was not until many days after that my worst fears were confirmed. Two bodies were found on the shore – one near Viareggio – which I went and examined. The face and hands, and parts of the body not protected by the dress, were fleshless'

DIARIES

'Only good girls keep diaries. Bad girls don't have the time'

TALLULAH BANKHEAD

1. Which book consists of Miranda Grey's diary and Frederick Clegg's recollections?

2. How many volumes of *Diaries* did Anais Nin write?

3. Who stated, 'I never travel without my diary. One should always have something sensational to read on the train'?

4. Whose diaries were submitted anonymously by Doris Lessing?

5. Whose first entry in her diary describes being interrupted in the planting of bulbs by an unwelcome visitor?

6. Who began a journal on 12 March, wrote mainly about food, and decided on 1 April not to keep a journal any more?

7. Who recommended keeping a diary 'should you wish to make sure that your birthday will be celebrated three hundred years hence'?

8. About whom did Mr Lockwood have an eerie dream after reading her journal?

9. Whose diaries were posthumously bowdlerized by her daughter Louise?

10. Who reported after his trip to hear Mrs Turner's daughter play the harpsichord, 'Lord! it was enough to make any man sick to hear her; yet I was forced to commend her highly'?

DIVORCE AND MARITAL INFIDELITY

'A mistress should be like a little country retreat near the town, not to dwell in constantly, but only for a night and away.'

WILLIAM WYCHERLEY
The Country Wife

1. Who observed, 'You never really know a man until you've divorced him'?

2. Who remarked where that 'a woman's career, particularly if it is successful, is often blamed for the break-up of a marriage, but never a man's'?

3. Who declared, 'Divorce is the sign of knowledge in our time'?

4. Who pointed out that 'divorce is America's great contribution to marriage'?

5. In which play is someone forced to spend 'a whole weekend in Brighton with a lady called Vera Williams'?

6. Who wrote a pamphlet entitled *The Doctrine and Discipline of Divorce*?

7. Who reflected that 'like a bee sting, the promiscuous leave behind in each encounter something of themselves by which they are made to suffer'?

8. Who pointed out that 'you can make divorce as easy to obtain as a dog licence, but you can't burn away the sense of shame and waste'?

9. Who stated, 'I have been so misused by men with one wife
That I would live with satyrs all my life'?

10. Which adulterous couple consummated their relationship during a rough transatlantic crossing?

DREAMS

'I dreamt that I dwelt in marble halls
With vassals and serfs at my side'

ALFRED BUNN
The Bohemian Girl

1. 'Last night I dreamt I went to Manderley again'. Who is speaking and in which novel?

2. Who dreamed 'that Greece might still be free'?

3. Who dreamt of 'Inestimable stones, unvalued jewels,
All scattered in the bottom of the sea'?

4. Who professed, 'One can write, think and pray exclusively of others; dreams are all egocentric'?

5. Who proclaimed,
'I have spread my dreams under your feet;
Tread softly because you tread on my dreams'?

6. Who opined, 'The dreamers of the day are dangerous men, for they may act their dream with open eyes, to make it possible'?

7. Who recalled a nightmare in which 'You dream you are crossing the Channel, and tossing about in a steamer from Harwich'?

8. In 1981 which novelist admitted that he was 'one of those people given to dreaming about the Queen'?

9. Who wrote, 'All men dream; but not equally. Those who dream at night in the dusty recesses of their minds wake in the day to find it was vanity'?

10. Who wrote that 'The boys are dreaming wicked or of the bucking ranches of the night and the jollyrodgered sea'?

DRINK

'Porter: Drink, sir, is a great provoker of three things.
Macduff: What three things does drink especially provoke?
Porter: Marry, sir, nose-painting, sleep and urine. Lechery, sir, it provokes and unprovokes; it provokes the desire, but it takes away the performance.'

WILLIAM SHAKESPEARE
Macbeth

1. Who thought who had indulged too freely in Mr Weston's good wine?

2. Who wrote a novel called *Mr Weston's Good Wine*?

3. Which major said, 'Alcohol is a very necessary article . . . it makes life bearable to millions of people who could not endure their existence if they were sober'?

4. Who advised whom to 'Drink no longer water, but use a little wine for thy stomach's sake'?

5. 'Your lips, on my own, when they printed "Farewell",
Had never been soiled by the "beverage of hell".'
Which temperance warning does this verse come from?

6. Who wrote, 'By the end of five days I had completely overcome my repugnance for the taste of whisky'?

7. Who claimed that 'work is the curse of the drinking classes'?

8. Who withdrew to the privacy of their own room to indulge in sucking oranges?

9. Who wanted to be 'in an alehouse in London! I would give all my fame for a pot of ale, and safety'?

10. The scholar Richard Burton said that there were 'two main plagues . . . which have infatuated and besotted myriads of people'. What were they?

ECCENTRICS AND EXTROVERTS

'We never knows wot's hidden in each other's hearts; and if we had glass winders there, we'd need keep the shutters up'

CHARLES DICKENS
Martin Chuzzlewit

1. Who defined a musicologist as 'a man who can read music but can't hear it'?

2. Which eccentric claimed in 1972 that he was 'not going to be quite as reclusive as I have been'?

3. Who said, 'It is better to die on your feet than to live on your knees'?

4. Who wrote, 'Once she arrived home at seven a.m. carrying a gate. Who am I to say there was anything wrong with her?'?

5. Which extrovert entertainer claimed 'My age is thirty-nine – plus tax'?

6. Who remarked about whom, 'I can't bear another moment of —'s inane chatter. If he wags his silly finger at me once more, I'll hit him'?

7. Which publishing extrovert was condemned by H.G. Wells as 'too loud and vain . . . to be a proper scoundrel'?

8. Who complained about 'an aspersion upon my parts of speech'?

9. Who 'had just
Completed my design
To keep the Menai Bridge from rust
By boiling it in wine'?

10. What is the profession of the eccentric who appears under three names in *Headlong Hall*, *Nightmare Abbey* and *Crotchet Castle* by Thomas Love Peacock?

EDUCATION

'A little learning is a dangerous thing'

ALEXANDER POPE
'An Essay on Criticism'

1. What was the name of the university (college) in *Who's Afraid of Virginia Woolf?* by Edward Albee?

2. Who was a student at Ingolstadt University?

3. Whose school report claimed that 'she has set herself an extremely low standard, which she has failed to maintain'?

4. Who was asked to present the prizes at Market Snodsbury Grammar School, and why?

5. Why did Paul Pennyfeather feel comparatively at home in prison?

6. The prospectus for which place of learning stipulated that 'Youth are boarded, clothed, booked, furnished with pocket-money, provided with all necessaries, instructed in all languages living and dead'?

7. Who is describing what? 'The fellows and monks of my time were decent easy men, who supinely enjoyed the gifts of the founder'?

8. 'Alas, regardless of their doom,
   The little victims play!'
Where?

9. In the eleven-volume *Strangers and Brothers* series of novels by C.P. Snow, what was the hero's name and profession?

10. Name Jim Dixon's rival in *Lucky Jim*, and the post of his father.

ENTERTAINMENTS

'I am never merry when I hear sweet music'

WILLIAM SHAKESPEARE
The Merchant of Venice

1. Which celebrated conductor remarked, 'I have played everywhere except in the street. I even played in pantomime at the old Surrey, and I don't regret a minute of it'?

2. Who organized some amateur theatricals while Sir Thomas Bertram was away?

3. Who observed, 'I wouldn't say when you've seen one Western you've seen the lot; but when you've seen the lot you get the feeling you've seen one'?

4. Who entertained his love with a song, accompanied by a small guitar?

5. Which wit remarked about a cinema star, 'That girl speaks eighteen languages and can't say no in any of them'?

6. Who observed that 'Opera in English is, in the main, just about as sensible as baseball in Italy'?

7. Which playwright emphasized that 'Refusing to have an opinion is a way of having one'?

8. Who were 'the best actors in the world, either for tragedy, comedy, history, pastoral, pastoral-comical, historical-pastoral, tragical-historical, tragical-comical-historical-pastoral'?

9. Who observed that 'Words can be deceitful, but pantomime necessarily is simple, clear and direct'?

10. Who stated that 'a novel is a static thing that one moves through: a play is a dynamic thing that moves past one'?

EPITAPHS, -GRAPHS AND -GRAMS

'Let's talk of graves, of worms and epitaphs'

WILLIAM SHAKESPEARE
Richard II

1. Who 'gave the little wealth he had
To build a house for fools and mad;
And showed, by one satiric touch,
No nation wanted it so much'?

2. Who wrote that 'anyone can tell the truth but only very few of us can make epigrams'?

3. Whose epitaph was 'Cast a cold eye
On life, on death.
Horseman pass by'?

4. Which writer would Salman Rushdie like to have beside him as 'Italy explodes' and 'the world ends'?

5. Why was Ben Jonson able to escape hanging after he killed a fellow actor in a duel?

6. Who wrote, 'Nature, and Nature's laws, lay hid in night,
God said, *Let Newton be!* and all was light'?

7. Who wrote *Epitaph of a Small Winner*, widely considered to be one of the outstanding Brazilian works of all time, and when?

8. Who defined wit as being 'the epitaph of an emotion'?

9. Which fellow painter wrote that when Sir Joshua Reynolds died

> 'All nature was degraded:
> The King dropp'd a tear into the Queen's Ear,
> And all his Pictures Faded'?

10. Who wrote, 'What I like about Clive
Is that he is no longer alive.
There is a great deal to be said
For being dead'?

FAME

'Fame is being asked to sign your name on the back of a cigarette packet'

BILLY CONNOLLY

1. Who compared fame to 'a river, that beareth up things light and swollen, and drowns things weighty and solid'?

2. Which poet wrote, 'Fame is the spur that the clear spirit doth raise'?

3. Who wrote a novel entitled *Fame is the Spur*?

4. Who proclaimed, 'I have learned all I know of literature from Conrad and England has learned all it knows about literature from me'?

5. Who wrote, 'I went to Frankfort and got drunk,
With that most learned professor, Brunck'?

6. Who remarked that he was famous for living opposite George Bernard Shaw?

7. Who lamented,
'Oh Fame! – if e'er I took delight in my praises,
'Twas less for the sake of thy high-sounding phrases'?

8. Who admitted that poets' food was 'love and fame'?

9. Which Shakespeare play opens:
'Let fame, that all hunt after in their lives
Live registr'd upon our brazen tombs'?

10. At the New York Customs who stated, 'I have nothing to declare but my genius'?

FAMILIES

'If a man's character is to be abused, say what you will, there's nobody like a relation to do the business.'

WILLIAM MAKEPEACE THACKERAY
Vanity Fair

1. In which novel is it claimed that 'all happy families resemble one another, but each unhappy family is unhappy in its own way'?

2. What was the relationship between Rudyard Kipling, Stanley Baldwin and Edward Burne-Jones?

3. Who, hoping to live with relatives after the death of her parents, wrote to an aunt in Sussex, and received a reply which ended, 'Child, child, if you come to this doomed house, what is to save you? Perhaps you may be able to help us when our hour comes'?

4. What literary siblings were lampooned by Noel Coward as the Swiss Family Whittlebot?

5. What was the biblical name of Jack Easy's father?

6. Who was 'Marmee'?

7. Which adopted family included an actress, a mechanic and a ballet dancer?

8. What was the profession of Honey's father in *Who's Afraid of Virginia Woolf?* by Edward Albee?

9. From what did the wealth of the Forsyte family originally derive?

10. Which character pointed out to whom, 'Nobody, who has not been in the interior of a family, can say what the difficulties of any individual of that family will be'?

FANTASY

'Opening on the foam
Of perilous seas, in faery lands forlorn'

JOHN KEATS
'Ode to a Nightingale'

1. What have the following in common a) a box with legs, b) a gigantic tortoise and c) a wizard with a spell he mustn't say?

2. In which novel is found the drug KR-3 that can alter the reality of the whole world?

3. Who had strange colouring and went to sea in a decidedly leaky vessel?

4. 'They sought it with thimbles, they sought it with care;
They pursued it with forks and hope.'
What were they after?

5. How many birds built their nests in the old man's beard?

6. Who lived in The Hill with a 'perfectly round door like a porthole, painted green, with a shiny yellow knob in the exact middle'?

7. Where did the aliens who attacked the earth with Red Weed during the last years of the seventeenth century come from?

8. What do Strider, Elessar and Arathorn's son have in common?

9. In what Gothic tale, first published in France, does the grandson of Haroun-al-Raschid become the servant of the Devil?

10. Which two planets were called Malacandra and Perelandra?

FIRST LINES

'It was the best of times, it was the worst of times'

CHARLES DICKENS
Opening words of *The Tale of Two Cities*

From which works, and by whom, are these the opening words?

1. 'I was not anxious to go'

2. 'This is the saddest story I have ever heard'

3. 'I address these words – written in India – to my relatives in England'

4. 'I am born'

5. 'It is a truth universally acknowledged that a single man in possession of a good fortune must be in want of a wife'

6. 'I met a traveller from an antique land'

7. 'All this happened, more or less'

8. 'The sky above the port was the color of television, tuned to a dead channel'

9. 'Call me Ishmael'

10. '"Take my camel, dear," said my aunt Dot, as she climbed down from this animal on her return from High Mass'

FOOD

'Do I dare to eat a peach?'

T.S. Eliot
'The Love Song of J. Alfred Prufrock'

1. Who admitted in which novel, 'Many's the long night I've dreamed of cheese – toasted, mostly'?

2. Who tried in vain to feast on ham and fish, and then broke up the pudding, the lobsters, the pears and the oranges?

3. In which novel was it claimed that 'the staple diet of the agricultural classes' is 'cider and tinned salmon'?

4. Who tried to mend a watch with butter?

5. Who said of whom that he
'was passionately fond of roe.
He always liked to chew some,
When writing something gruesome'?

6. Which author likened where to being a movable feast?

7. In which play is it stated that 'there is no love sincerer than the love of food'?

8. Who described Italy as being 'so tender – like cooked macaroni – yards and yards of soft tenderness ravelled round everything'?

9. Whose redcurrant fool contained a bottle and a half of champagne and half a pint of old brandy?

10. In 1911 who claimed that the French 'if they cared to try, could produce an excellent and nutritious substitute out of cigar stumps and empty matchboxes'?

HATRED AND MURDER

**'Any kiddie in school can love like a fool,
But hating, my boy, is an art'**

OGDEN NASH
'Plea for Less Malice Toward None'

1. Which knee-cracking retainer murders his arch rival, Swelter, in the Hall of Spiders?

2. Who declared, 'It does not matter much what a man hates, provided he hates something'?

3. Who suggested that 'hate has what lust entirely lacks – persistence and continuity'?

4. Who commented in his *Autobiography* that 'few people can be happy unless they hate some other person, matter or creed'?

5. Who is caught up as a witness to the feud between the Grangerford and the Shepherdson families?

6. Who said of whom, 'I hate him for he is a Christian'?

7. Who lamented, 'To be choked with hate
May well be of all evil chances chief'?

8. 'He left it dead, and with its head
He went galumphing back.' Who has been killed?

9. In which play is it stated that 'hatred is the coward's revenge for being intimidated'?

10. Who claimed, 'When you have to kill a man it costs nothing to be polite'?

HEROISM

'Claret is the liquor for boys, port for men, but he who aspires to be a hero must drink brandy'

SAMUEL JOHNSON

1. Who was known as the Norfolk Hero?

2. Which eponymous hero is eaten alive?

3. Who said it was worth dying 'for the ashes of his fathers and the temples of his gods'?

4. Each of the following writers refer to 'The Master': a) Rudyard Kipling b) Evelyn Waugh c) Cole Leslie. Name the three Masters.

5. Which poet, when merely fifteen, 'thought everything was over and finished for everyone' when he learnt about the death in 1824 of George Gordon, Lord Byron?

6. Who remarked, where, 'Down these mean streets a man must go who is not himself mean, who is neither tarnished nor afraid'?

7. Who declared, 'As you get older it is harder to have heroes, but it is sort of necessary'?

8. Who claims to be 'a hero with coward's legs . . . a hero from the waist up'?

9. Who stated that 'Unnatural vices
Are fathered by our heroism'?

10. In whose political novel is it remarked, 'Thoughts of heroes were as good as warming-pans'?

HISTORY

'The Duke returned from the wars today and did pleasure me in his top-boots'

SARAH, THE DUCHESS OF MARLBOROUGH (1660–1744)

1. What was the name of the fourth musketeer?

2. Who was 'The Once and Future King', and what was his childhood name?

3. Which 'pritty witty king . . . never said a foolish thing,
And never did a wise one'?

4. At the age of fifteen in 1790 which novelist wrote *A History of England* but in apology stated it was 'by a partial, ignorant and prejudiced historian'?

5. 'There was a sound of revelry by night,
And Belgium's Capital had gathered then
Her Beauty and Chivalry'
To which moment does this refer?

6. Who wrote:
'"Peace upon earth!" was said. We sing it,
And pay a million guests to bring it.
After two thousand years of mass
We've got as far as poison-gas.'
Where does this come from?

7. Who pointed out to whom that 'Mr Carlyle is old, and childless, and poor; but he is very popular and respected by the nation'?

8. Who 'from the time he was three years old read incessantly, for the most part lying on a rug before the fire, with his book on the ground, and a piece of bread and butter in his hand'?

9. Who thought that 'history is more or less bunk'?

10. Who remarked, 'We learn from history that we learn nothing from history'?

HONS, REBELS AND OTHERS

1. Name this author and the title of his first book.

2. Despite an inability to spell, this author became famous when her first book was published. Who is she?

THE HULTON-DEUTSCH COLLECTION

COURTESY PENGUIN BOOKS

AXEL POIGNANT ARCHIVE

3. At the age of sixteen he was articled to an architect. Who is he?

4. He became a chronic alcoholic and died by misadventure. Name his first work.

5. What is the title of the literary self-portrait by this author? In which year was he awarded the Nobel Prize for Literature?

6. Who is this and what was his profession?

7. Who are these authors and what do they have in common?

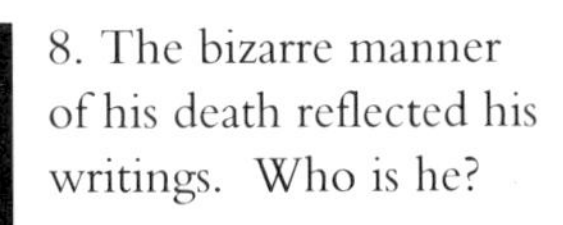

8. The bizarre manner of his death reflected his writings. Who is he?

THE HULTON-DEUTSCH COLLECTION

9. Among her published work is the novelized life of a dean. Name the book, the author and the dean.

CECIL BEATON/CAMERA PRESS

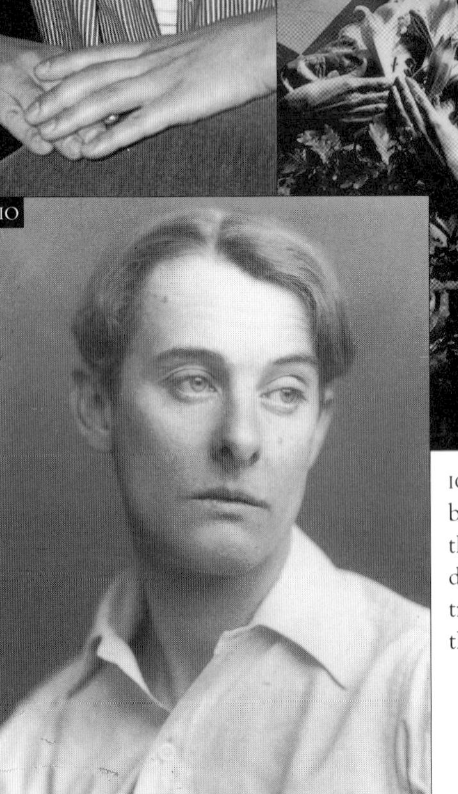

THE HULTON-DEUTSCH COLLECTION

10. He translated a play by a close friend – and the friendship led to disaster. Name the translator, the friend and the play.

HORSES

'A horse is at least *human*, for God's sake'

J.D. SALINGER
The Catcher in the Rye

1. Who was Master of the Flat Hat Hunt?

2. Who remarked that 'England is the paradise of women, the purgatory of men, and the hell of horses'?

3. Who 'flung himself upon his horse and rode madly off in all directions'?

4. 'With his nostrils full of blood to the brim
And with circles of red for his eye-sockets' rim'
Which horse was this, and what brought him to this sorry state?

5. Name the authors of *Bring on the Empty Horses, The Wooden Horse* and *They Shoot Horses, Don't They?*

6. Who was the owner of grey Capilet?

7. What was the name of Tam o'Shanter's mare?

8. Whose 'horse in the silence champed the grasses
Of the forest's ferny floor'?

9. 'She threw me in front of the Judges,
And my silly old collar-bone's bust'
Name the offending horse.

10. Which of King Arthur's knights had a horse called Gringolet?

INSULTS AND ABUSE

'I don't like the family Stein!
There is Gert, there is Ep, there is Ein.
Gert's writings are punk,
Ep's statues are junk,
Nor can anyone understand Ein'

ANON

1. Who said of whom, 'He has occasional flashes of silence, that make his conversation perfectly delightful'?

2. Who claimed that 'most women are not so young as they are painted'?

3. Who stated that 'you always knew where you were with Goldwyn – nowhere'?

4. Who described the Shakespeare Memorial Theatre as 'a courageous and partly successful attempt to disguise a gasworks as a racquets court'?

5. Who fulminated and to whom, 'The devil damn thee black, thou cream-faced loon'?

6. In which play is it stated that 'the English have no respect for their language. It is impossible for an Englishman to open his mouth without making some other Englishman despise him'?

7. Which scholar defined the dog as being 'that indefatigable and unsavoury engine of pollution'?

8. Who stated about whom, 'He hasn't an enemy in the world, and none of his friends like him'?

9. Which American playwright commented, 'Watching my plays in London is like seeing them in translation'?

10. Where will you find this? 'One of the best warehouses I ever saw was the Vatican in Rome'

JEALOUSY

**''Tis not through envy of Thy happy lot,
But being too happy in Thy happiness'**

John Keats
'Ode to a Nightingale'

1. Whose jealous madness is fuelled by the loss of a handkerchief?

2. Which French novelist remarked that 'to jealousy, nothing is more frightful than laughter'?

3. Who claimed that 'Art is a jealous mistress'?

4. Who are the rivals in Sheridan's play of that name?

5. Which writer defined jealousy as 'no more than feeling alone against smiling enemies'?

6. Where is it claimed that 'love is as strong as death; jealousy is cruel as the grave'?

7. Who declared, 'Envy's a sharper spur than pay'?

8. Who described jealousy as a 'dragon which slays love under the pretence of keeping it alive'?

9. In which novel is jealousy described as 'an obsession that grips you clammily . . . It feels like something solid and curdled, lodged in your stomach. It blocks your lungs'?

10. Who said, 'So full of artless jealousy is guilt,
It spills itself in fearing to be spilt'?

JUSTICE

'In the cause of justice none of us should see salvation'

William Shakespeare
The Merchant of Venice

1. Whose bloody idea of justice is to feed his enemies their children baked in a pie?

2. Which novel's epigraph is 'Vengeance is mine, I will repay'?

3. Who said, 'My life I never held but as a pawn to wage against thine enemies' to whom?

4. Who is condemned to wear the letter 'A' for the rest of her life?

5. In which novel by Walter Scott is there an example of 'Jedwood justice – hang in haste, and try at leisure'?

6. In which novel by Charles Dickens, which character stated, 'If the law supposes that, the law is a ass – a idiot'?

7. Who declared that 'the price of justice is eternal publicity'?

8. Which novel claimed that 'absolute freedom mocks at justice. Absolute justice denies freedom'?

9. In which book is it claimed that 'no brilliance is needed in law. Nothing but common sense and relatively clean finger-nails'?

10. '"I'll be judge, I'll be jury," said cunning old Fury;
"I'll try the whole cause, and condemn you to death"'
Who says this and to whom?

LAST LINES AND WORDS

'For when this song is sung and past,
My lute be still, for I have done'

THOMAS WYATT
'The Lover Complayneth the Unkindness of his Love'

1. 'So we beat on, boats against the current, borne back ceaselessly into the past'. Of which novel are these the closing words?

2. In which book's last line did the narrator wonder how 'anyone could ever imagine unquiet slumbers for the sleepers in that quiet earth'?

3. 'Not with a bang but a whimper' describes what?

4. Which novel ends, 'I go to encounter for the millionth time the reality of experience and to forge in the smithy of my soul the uncreated conscience of my race. . . Old father, old artificer, stand me now and ever in good stead'?

5. Which novel ends with the words, 'if it wasn't for the rings we would not have identified him'?

6. What book ends with the hero stabbed in the heart 'like a dog'?

7. Who exclaimed, 'We are all going to Heaven, and Vandyke is of the company'?

8. Whose last words were 'I die happy'?

9. What novel ends with notes from the University of Denay in 2195?

10. Which writer said these words on her deathbed: 'I love the rain. I want the feeling of it on my face'?

LEADERSHIP

'Twenty-two acknowledged concubines and a library of sixty-two thousand volumes attested the variety of his inclinations; and from the productions which he left behind him, it appears that both the one and the other were designed for use rather than for ostentation'

EDWARD GIBBON ON THE EMPEROR GORDIAN THE YOUNGER
The Decline and Fall of the Roman Empire

1. Who became the first President of the Union of Soviet Writers in 1934?

2. Of which town does Michael Henchard become a leading dignitary?

3. Which leader was described as 'a cross between a fantasy of the bedroom and a saint'?

4. Who observed that 'headmasters have powers at their disposal with which Prime Ministers have never yet been invested'?

5. Who 'must be able to act just like a beast' and 'should learn from the fox and the lion'?

6. Who was the leader when 'even the ranks of Tuscany
Could scarce forbear to cheer'?

7. Who claimed, 'People, like sheep, tend to follow their leader – occasionally in the right direction'?

8. Who quipped in 1947, 'Only one in a thousand is a leader of men – the other 999 follow women'?

9. Who wrote about whom, 'The rising hope of those stern and unbending Tories who follow, reluctantly and mutinously, a leader whose experience and eloquence are indispensable to opinions they abhor'?

10. Which leader stated, 'If you can't stand the heat, get out of the kitchen'?

LETTERS

'I am not arguing with you – I am telling you'

JAMES MCNEILL WHISTLER
The Gentle Art of Making Enemies

1. Who wrote letters to friends, relatives, psychiatrists, politicians, Heidegger, Nietzsche, newspapers and God but finally had 'no messages for anyone'?

2. Whom did the *noms de plume* conceal when 'Mr Wu' corresponded with 'Mrs Stitch'?

3. Who wrote of 'Letters of thanks, letters from banks,
Letters of joy from girl and boy'?

4. 'Be not alarmed, Madam, on receiving this letter, by the apprehension of its containing any repetition of those sentiments . . . which were last night so disgusting to you.' Who thus addressed his lady love?

5. Which person wrote a scathing letter in February 1755 which included the phrase that seven years had passed since he'd been 'repulsed from your door'?

6. Who, writing to Thomas Flower Ellis in 1850, remarked, 'I have seen the hippopotamus, both asleep and awake; and I can assure you that, awake or asleep, he is the ugliest of the works of God'?

7. Who wrote to his son stating that 'if Shakespeare's genius had been cultivated, those beauties, which we so justly admire in him, would have been undisguised by those extravagances and that nonsense with which they are frequently accompanied'?

8. Which pair of letter-writers addressed each other as 'Clarinda' and 'Sylvander'?

9. Who wrote to Aldous Huxley stating that he'd 'like to write an essay on Arnold Bennett – sort of pig in clover'?

10. Who claimed in a letter, 'I am fond of children (except boys)'?

LIES AND TRUTHS

'Truth exists; only lies are invented'

GEORGES BRAQUE

1. Which sixteen-year-old described himself as 'the most terrific liar you ever saw in your life'?

2. About whom was it said that 'there were things which he stretched, but mainly he told the truth'?

3. Who claimed that there were 'three kinds of lies: lies, damned lies and statistics'?

4. Which writer offered the opinion that 'truth can be the worst destroyer of all'?

5. Who wrote that 'she's too crafty a woman to invent a new lie when an old one will serve'?

6. Who 'told such Dreadful Lies
It made one Gasp and Stretch one's Eyes'?

7. Who claimed that she 'never had any mother' and 'never was born'?

8. In which play does a character state, 'Truth is not compatible with the defence of the realm'?

9. Which author claimed that 'when truth is discovered by someone else it loses some of its effectiveness'?

10. Which Shakespearean character offers various gradients of lying from 'the retort courteous' to 'the lie direct'?

LOCALES

'Consult the genius of the place in all'

ALEXANDER POPE
'Epistle to Lord Burlington'

1. In which district of New York does Donald Barthelme's Snow White live?

2. What is Airstrip One?

3. In which part of London did Daryl Davies M.A. get a job?

4. Where did Adela Quested accuse Aziz of molesting her?

5. Who spent a quarter of a century as a parson in Weston Longueville, Norfolk?

6. 'First of all there is Blue. Later there is White, and then there is Black, and before the beginning there is Brown.' This is from a trilogy of novels that is set where?

7. On which river does St Oggs stand?

8. Who wrote, 'London, that cesspool into which all the loungers of the Empire are irresistibly drawn'?

9. In Oscar Wilde's *A Woman of No Importance* which city

is named to receive the souls of good Americans after their death?

10. Which famous journey started at a pub in London and finished in a cathedral in Kent?

LOVE

'Love and a cough cannot be hid'

LATIN PROVERB

1. Mrs Greenower had two suitors. What were their names, and who eventually gained the hand of the fair widow?

2. According to which poet 'we must love one another or die'?

3. Who prayed he be given 'chastity and continency – but not yet'?

4. Who was married to Arabella but in love with Mrs Marwood?

5. Who 'loved with a love that was more than love'?

6. 'Let us not speak, for the love we bear one another –
   Let us hold hands and look'
Who were these lovers?

7. Who declared that 'men have died from time to time, and worms have eaten them, but not for love'?

8. Who was courted by Georgie Pillson?

9. According to the Comte de Bussy-Rabutin in the seventeenth century what 'is to love as wind is to fire; it extinguishes the small, it enkindles the great'?

10. Who warned people not to be 'swallowed up in books! An ounce of love is worth a pound of knowledge'?

LUST AND CHASTITY

'Lust is but a bloody fire
Kindled with unchaste desire,
Fed in heart, whose flames aspire,
As thoughts do blow them higher and higher'

WILLIAM SHAKESPEARE
The Merry Wives of Windsor

1. Who was enchanted by Sarah Woodruff?

2. Who had an incestuous affair with his sister Franny?

3. In which play did incestuous lust end in tragedy?

4. Which character was enamoured of Alisoun in *The Miller's Tale* by Geoffrey Chaucer?

5. In which novel did the chastity of the heroine become the subject of a wager?

6. Whose passion for Daisy Buchanan finished up as a case of murder?

7. Who admitted, 'I've looked on a lot of women with lust. I've committed adultery in my heart many times'?

8. Who wrote, 'Oh whip the dogs away my Lord,
They make me ill with lust'?

9. Who complained, 'Some of them go quite rigid with disgust
At anything but marriage'?

10. 'Then worms shall try
That long preserv'd virginity:
And your quaint honour turn to dust;
And into ashes all my lust'
Where would this happen?

MARRIAGE

'It is a woman's business to get married as soon as possible, and a man's to keep unmarried as long as he can'

GEORGE BERNARD SHAW
Man and Superman

1. Who failed to celebrate a wedding anniversary at The Bell at Edmonton?

2. Which bride threw crumbs of her wedding cake to the doves during her groom's speech?

3. Who declared that marriage resembled 'a pair of shears, so joined that they cannot be separated; often moving in opposite

directions, yet always punishing anyone who comes between them'?

4. Who described her recent marriage as 'the deep peace of the double bed after the hurly-burly of the chaise longue'?

5. 'They took me from my wife, and to save trouble
   I wed again, and made the error double'
Name the poet.

6. What was so shocking about Lilia Herriton's marriage to Gino in *Where Angels Fear to Tread* by E.M. Forster?

7. Who, perhaps unwisely, embarks upon marriage feeling for her future husband 'the reverence of a neophyte entering on a high grade of initiation'?

8. Who is the husband of Lady Torfrida?

9. 'Reader, I married him'. Who married whom?

10. Who opined that 'happiness in marriage is entirely a matter of chance'?

MEDLEY

'A snapper-up of unconsidered trifles'

WILLIAM SHAKESPEARE
The Winter's Tale

1. Who started his adventure in South Africa, then went to England and Scotland with the final denouement taking place in Kent?

2. Who wrote, 'Oh, life is a glorious cycle of song,
A medley of extemporanea;
And love is a thing that can never go wrong;
And I am Marie of Roumania'?

3. Which adventurer remarked, 'With the possible exception of the equator, everything begins somewhere'?

4. Who etched Fagin in the condemned cell?

5. Who was the Knight of the Doleful Countenance?

6. In *Erewhon* by Samuel Butler, name the beautiful girl gaoler who helps the narrator when he is first thrown into gaol.

7. Who opined in a letter to Bishop Mandell Creighton, 'Power tends to corrupt and absolute power corrupts absolutely'?

8. Who declared that 'the all-male religions have produced no

religious imagery . . . The great religious art of the world is deeply involved with the female principle'?

9. Who explained, 'The famous soft watches are nothing else than the tender, extravagant, solitary paranoia-critical camembert of time and space'?

10. Who ruminated, 'Life is rather like a tin of sardines – we're all of us looking for the key'?

MEMOIRS AND SELF-PORTRAITS

'You go not, till I set you up a glass
Where you may see the inmost part of you'

WILLIAM SHAKESPEARE
Hamlet

1. In which autobiographical novel does the protagonist state that 'Ireland is an old sow who eats her farrow'?

2. Who, in his *Autobiography*, describes his time at Oxford thus: 'I spent fourteen months at Magdalen College: they proved the fourteen months the most idle and unprofitable of my whole life'?

3. Whose life started in 'Wales, Wales, full of ugly chapels, of hidden money, of psalm-singing and rain'?

4. Robert Graves fought in the First World War as a captain in the Royal Welch Fusiliers. Which friend held the same rank in the same regiment?

5. Who dedicated his autobiography to 'My Friends, Known and Unknown'?

6. Who claimed that 'twenty-five seems to me the latest age at which anybody should write an autobiography'?

7. Which French marshal observed, 'To write one's memoirs is to speak ill of everybody except oneself'?

8. Which French chronicler wrote memoirs in twenty-one volumes that offered lively insights into the court of Louis XIV?

9. What is the correct title of the novel known as *Fanny Hill* which John Cleland wrote for twenty guineas although it brought the publisher over £10,000?

10. Which novelist remarked that whereas fiction never lies, and 'reveals the writer totally, autobiography can distort; facts can be realigned'?

MUSIC

'Music and women I cannot give way to, whatever my business is'

SAMUEL PEPYS
Diaries, 9 March 1666

1. Which novel remarked that 'music was invented to confirm human loneliness'?

2. Who 'could not make
Antonio Stradivari's violins
Without Antonio Stradivari'?

3. Who 'did not see any reason why the devil should have all the good tunes'?

4. In which play is it stated, 'Music has charms to soothe a savage breast'?

5. Who wrote about whom that 'his music used to be original. Now it is aboriginal'?

6. Who defined Bach as being 'the greatest and purest moment in music of all times'?

7. Which violinist declared 'a composer is unable to hide anything – by his music ye shall know him'?

8. Who remarked that 'the worst part of being gay in the twentieth century is all that damn disco music to which one has to listen'?

9. Who complained about Beethoven's Seventh Symphony, 'What can you do with it? It's like a lot of yaks jumping around'?

10. Of which two composers did Maurice Baring write, 'We see the contrast between the genius which does what it must and the talent which does what it can'?

ODDMENTS

'Read no history: nothing but biography, for that is life without theory'

BENJAMIN DISRAELI
Contarini Fleming

1. Who believed his conception was blighted by the winding of a clock?

2. Which English clergyman, famous for muddling his words, described an acquaintance as having been eaten by missionaries?

3. 'Death hath this also, that it openeth the gate to good fame, and extinguisheth envy'. Who said this?

4. Who complained, 'One would be in less danger
From the wiles of a stranger,
If one's own kin and kith
Were more fun to be with'?

5. Who or what, after a ten-year journey compressed into twenty-four hours, was seized by the Customs authorities in Folkestone?

6. On his deathbed who remarked, staring at the wallpaper in the room, 'One of us must go'?

7. In which novel is it claimed that 'ending is better than mending'?

8. Who was viciously attacked by D.H. Lawrence for suffering from the disease that was to later kill her?

9. Who 'has caught
The Sultan's turret in a noose of light'?

10. Who stated, 'Oft-times nothing profits more
Than self-esteem'?

ODD ONE OUT

'I wish I loved the Human Race;
I wish I loved its silly face;
I wish I liked the way it walks;
I wish I liked the way it talks;
And when I'm introduced to one
I wish I thought *What Jolly Fun*!'

WALTER RALEIGH
'Wishes of an Elderly Man'

Which is the odd one out?

1. Jose Eustacio Rivera, Mario Vargas Llosa, Gabriel Garcia Marquez, Jose Asuncion Rivera

2. Laputa, Houyhnhnms, Brobdingnag, Smeagol, Lagoda, Glubbdubrib

3. Robert Coover, Jack Kerouac, James McNeill Whistler, Robert Lowell

4. Father Merrill, Hungry Joe, Doc Daneasca, General Peacham

5. *The Old Curiosity Shop*, *Our Mutual Friend*, *The Small House at Allington*, *Great Expectations*

6. Hadley Richardson, Martha Gellhorn, Lillian Hellman, Mary Welsh, Pauline Pfeiffer

7. Peter Wimsey, Adam Dalgliesh, Sherlock Holmes, Albert Campion

8. The Water Rat, the Hare, the Mole, the Otter, the Badger

9. Mr Knightley, Mr Tilney, Captain Wentworth, Colonel Brandon, Mr Lovelace

10. *Flappers and Philosophers*, *Taps at Reveille*, *The Sound and the Fury* and *The Crack-Up and Other Pieces*

OLD AGE

'In a dream you are never eighty'

ANNE SEXTON
'Old'

1. Which old man 'turned a back-somersault in at the door'?

2. 'I am a very foolish fond old man'. Who was?

3. Who decided that, in growing old, 'I shall wear the bottoms of my trousers rolled'?

4. Who wrote, 'An aged man is but a paltry thing,
A tattered coat upon a stick'?

5. 'And when they get to feeling old,
They up and shoot themselves, I'm told'
Who are 'they'?

6. 'I saw that the bride within the bridal dress had withered like tne dress, and like the flowers, and had no brightness left but the brightness of her sunken eyes'. Which old lady was this?

7. 'On his nose there was a cricket,
In his hat a Railway-Ticket'
Who was this?

8. Who described which monarch as 'an old, mad, blind, despised, and dying king'?

9. Who was described as 'an elderly man of 42'?

10. Who wrote, 'Old men and comets have been reverenced for the same reason; their long beards, and pretences to foretell events'?

OPTIMISM AND PESSIMISM

'The optimist proclaims that we live in the best of all possible worlds; and the pessimist fears this is true'

JAMES BRANCH CABELL

1. Why did the author of *A Confederacy of Dunces* take his own life before the book was published?

2. Who stated that 'pessimism does win us some great moments'?

3. Who declared about someone who chose to remarry immediately after the death of a wife to whom he had been married most unhappily that it must be the 'triumph of hope over experience'?

4. Who wrote that 'pessimism, when you get used to it, is just as agreeable as optimism'?

5. Which politician remarked, 'So little time, so much to do'?

6. Who ran his life on the principle 'in case anything turned up'?

7. Which English king, on first seeing his intended, announced, 'Harris, I am not well; pray get me a glass of brandy'?

8. Who stated, 'Prison is not a mere physical horror. It is using a pickaxe to no purpose that makes a prison'?

9. Who defined a pessimist as 'a man who looks both ways before crossing a one-way street'?

10. Who remarked that 'anyone who hates dogs and babies can't be all bad'?

PETS

'Mothers of large families (who claim to common sense)
Will find a tiger well repays the trouble and expense'

HILAIRE BELLOC
A Bad Child's Book of Beasts

1. Who wrote a biographical novel about Elizabeth Barrett Browning's pet spaniel, and what was the dog's name?

2. Which animals 'offer no angles to the wind'?

3. Who was worried about Central Park ducks in winter?

4. Which historian claimed that he 'would never wound a cat's feelings, no matter how downright aggressive' he was feeling?

5. 'I had an aunt in Yucatan
   Who bought a — from a man
   And kept it for a pet'
What was this creature?

6. Who enquired, 'What female heart can gold despise?
   What cat's averse to fish?'?

7. 'Bully's cage supported stood
   On props of smoothest-shaven wood'
Who was Bully, and what happened to him?

8. Name the owners of these cats: Hodge, Old Foss and Jeoffrey.

9. Who, when her poor dog developed a distressing malady, would issue confidential bulletins, tinged with scepticism: 'He said he got it from a lamp-post'?

10. In which suspense novel is it claimed that 'what cats most appreciate in the human being is not the ability to produce food which they take for granted but his or her entertainment value'?

PLACES

'"What's the good of *Mercator*'s North Poles and Equators,
Tropics, Zones and Meridian lines?"
So the Bellman would cry: and the crew would reply,
"They are merely conventional signs!"'

LEWIS CARROLL
'The Hunting of the Snark'

1. Who wrote of the fictional world of Tion, Uqbar, and Orbis Tertius?

2. Which six-volume series of novels begins with Mary Ann Singleton arriving in San Francisco for the first time?

3. Who went to live at Dorincourt as a young boy?

4. In which novel are the conditions on Jacob's Island described?

5. What was the name of the small town that was the birthplace of Emily Dickinson?

6. Who lived in the village of Raveloe?

7. Which family resided at Norland Park?

8. From where did the Time Traveller in *The Time Machine* by H.G. Wells begin his journey?

9. Who wrote of 'the night we went to Birmingham by way of Beachy Head'?

10. Who slept alone because his girl was in Tungria?

POETRY AND POETS

'Poetry is the stuff in books that doesn't quite reach the margins'

ANONYMOUS CHILD'S ESSAY

1. Which poet published a memoir entitled *Grey is the Colour of Hope*?

2. Who wrote of whom, 'Mad Ireland hurt you into poetry
Now Ireland has the madness and her weather still
For poetry makes nothing happen'?

3. Which poet wrote, 'Poetry is not a career, but a mug's game'?

4. Who wrote that he rhymed for fun?

5. What, according to James Elroy Flecker, will happen to a nation whose people have forgotten poetry and whose poets have forgotten the people?

6. Which nineteenth-century aristocrat described Alfred Tennyson as 'out-babying Wordsworth and out-glittering Keats'?

7. Who called poets 'the trumpets which sing to battle, and feel not what they inspire . . . the unacknowledged legislators of the world'?

8. Who described W.H. Auden as someone 'able to write politically, carelessly and exquisitely'?

9. Who wrote, 'Poetry is the breath and finer spirit of all knowledge'?

10. Who observed, 'It's hard to say why writing verse
Should terminate in drink or worse'?

POLITICS

'Politics is perhaps the only profession for which no preparation is thought necessary'

ROBERT LOUIS STEVENSON
Familiar Studies of Men and Books

1. Who was arrested by the 'No 1s'?

2. What novel was built around the Gordon Riots of 1780?

3. Who declared that liberalism 'is *the* destructive force of the age'?

4. Who wrote, 'A politician is an arse upon which everyone has sat except man'?

5. Who stayed in the town of Dillborough?

6. Who wrote, 'Ultimate power is apt to corrupt the minds of those who possess it'?

7. Who was found by the Bureau of Statistics to be 'one against whom there was no official complaint'?

8. What was the name of Roderick Spode's political organization?

9. Who joined POUM but rejected PSUC?

10. In which book does Ezra Pound broadcast Nazi propaganda from Rome?

POVERTY

'Poverty keeps together more homes than it breaks up'

SAKI
The Chronicles of Clovis

1. Which novelist remarked that 'the very poor are unthinkable and only to be approached by the statistician and the poet'?

2. Who wrote that he had 'achieved poverty with distinction, but never poverty with dignity'?

3. Who claimed that 'poverty is the great reality. That's why the artist seeks it'?

4. 'Then the great man helped the poor,
   And the poor man loved the great'
When was this?

5. Who was supposed to live in 'a numble abode'?

6. Who said, and in which play, 'Who steals my purse steals trash'?

7. Which poet was 'poor, ailing and ignorant,
   Shut out from all the luxury of the world,
   The ill-bred son of a livery stable-keeper'
according to whom?

8. Who was 'one of the undeserving poor . . . up agen middle-class morality all the time'?

9. Which novel claims that 'the poor insist on being buried. It's usually the only way they can ensure getting a garden of their own'?

10. Who is referring to whom when he writes,
   'In honoured poverty thy voice did weave
   Songs consecrate to truth and liberty'?

PROFESSIONS

'It is the business of the wealthy man
To give employment to the artisan'

HILAIRE BELLOC
'Lord Finchley'

1. Who left Lowood Institution to work at Thornfield Hall?

2. If Nicole's husband wasn't a diver, what was he?

3. For which library in Hull did Philip Larkin work at the time of his death?

4. What was the profession of Kenneth Toomey?

5. Who taught at the Marcia Blaine School?

6. What was Mrs Warren's profession?

7. What was Mr Casaubon's lifelong work?

8. Who initially despised the manufacturer Mr Thornton's profession?

9. Which celebrated novelist's first job was that of junior clerk in the General Post Office?

10. Who claimed that 'a publisher is a useful middle-man. It is not for him to anticipate the verdict of criticism'?

PSEUDONYMS

'What's in a name?'

WILLIAM SHAKESPEARE
Romeo and Juliet

1. Name the publicity-shy man who wrote *The Treasure of the Sierra Madre*.

2. What was George Orwell's real name?

3. How did Allen Stewart Konigsberg justify writing About Death, directing Without Feathers and acting Asleep?

4. Under what names did Charlotte, Anne and Emily Brontë originally submit their novels to a publisher?

5. Under what pseudonym did crime writer Dashiell Hammett publish further short stories?

6. What was the real name of the author who wrote *The King Must Die* and *The Bull from the Sea*?

7. By what pseudonym is the playwright Gordon Daviot better known?

8. What was the real name of the man who wrote *The Adventures of Tom Sawyer* and its sequel *The Adventures of Huckleberry Finn*?

9. Which pseudonym did Cyril Connolly use when *The Unquiet Grave* was first published?

10. Under what name is David John Moore Cornwell better known?

REALISM

'Human kind
Cannot bear very much reality'

T.S. ELIOT
'Burnt Norton'

1. What is the occupation of the hero who sows his wild oats in *Saturday Night and Sunday Morning*?

2. Which novel was inspired by the author's experiences of the bombing of Dresden in 1945?

3. In which year was *The Naked and the Dead* published, and how old was its author, Norman Mailer?

4. Who wrote to Lady Ottoline Morrell, 'You mustn't think I advocate perpetual sex. Far from it. Nothing nauseates me more than perpetual sex in and out of season'?

5. Which novel claims that 'a Jewish man with parents alive is a fifteen-year-old boy, and will remain a fifteen-year-old boy until they die'?

6. Who is the narrator-commentator in *A Dance to the Music of Time*?

7. The words of which poem have been misheard and become the title of a novel featuring Holden Caulfield?

8. In which play is it stated, 'Reality is pretty brutal, pretty filthy, when you come to grips with it. Yet it's glorious all the same. It's so real and satisfactory'?

9. Who wrote, 'The nineteenth-century dislike of Realism is the rage of Caliban seeing his own face in the glass'?

10. In which book is it stated, 'Everything is a dangerous drug except reality, which is unendurable'?

RELIGION

'Religion is the frozen thought of men out of which they build temples'

KRISHNAMURTI

1. Who was the Canon of Cloisterham?

2. Who concluded that 'it's no go the Yogi-Man, it's no go Blavatsky,
All we want is a bank balance and a bit of skirt in a taxi'?

3. Who was always about in the Quad?

4. Who created the following ecclesiastical characters: a) The Rector's Wife, b) The Curate's Wife, c) The Perpetual Curate and d) Father Giles?

5. Who stated that 'if you really want to make a million . . . the quickest way is to start your own religion'?

6. Which Irish writer professed to be 'a Communist by day and a Catholic as soon as it gets dark'?

7. In 1936 which novelist claimed that 'for English Catholics, sacraments are the psychological equivalent of tractors in Russia'?

8. Who declared that 'as the French say, there are three sexes – men, women and clergymen'?

9. In 1778 who wrote, 'Once in every seven years I burn all my sermons; for it is a shame if I cannot write better sermons now than I did seven years ago'?

10. Who defined the English Bible as 'a book, which if everything else in our language should perish, would alone suffice to show the whole extent of its power and beauty'?

REMARKS

'Remarks are not literature'

GERTRUDE STEIN
The Autobiography of Alice B. Toklas

1. Who said, where, 'Ask not what your country can do for you – ask what you can do for your country'?

2. Who remarked about whom that his 'abiding complex and the source of much of his misery was that he was not a six-foot tall, extremely handsome and rich duke'?

3. Where did the remark 'from China to Peru' first appear, and what does it imply?

4. 'Nothing to do but work
Nothing to eat but food
Nothing to wear but clothes
To keep one from going nude'
Whose pessimistic remarks were these?

5. Who was 'the man who broke the bank at Monte Carlo', how and when?

6. From which novel is this taken, 'Life ain't all beer and skittles, and more's the pity'?

7. When Oscar Wilde remarked admiringly, 'How I wish I had said that,' who replied, 'You will, Oscar, you will'?

8. Who denied having remarked that 'the battle of Waterloo was won on the playing-fields of Eton'?

9. Who said to whom, 'Another damned, thick, square book! Always scribble, scribble, scribble! Eh!'

10. Who remarked, 'My centre is giving way, my right is in retreat; situation excellent, I shall attack'?

THE SEA

'I must go down to the sea again, to the lonely sea and the sky'

JOHN MASEFIELD
'Sea Fever'

1. Which fictional character signed on as a ship's boy on the *Highlander*?

2. Who captained the *Ghost*?

3. What seafaring trilogy takes a young man on a moral journey while crossing from England to Australia?

4. Who chartered the *Hispaniola*?

5. Who was hardly ever sick at sea?

6. Who sang to whom, 'Full fathom five thy father lies;
Of his bones are coral made . . .
Sea-nymphs hourly ring his knell'?

7. Who was the captain of the *Pequod*?

8. Who advised, 'Man marks the earth with ruin – his control
Stops with the shore'?

9. Who described 'the sloeblack, slow, black, crowblack, fishingboat-bobbing sea'?

10. Who are playing dice aboard the approaching skeleton ship, whose disappearance leads to the death of the ancient mariner's crewmates?

SERVANTS

'In my opinion Butlers ought
To know their place, and not to play
The Old Retainer night and day'

HILAIRE BELLOC
Cautionary Tales

1. Who kept six serving-men? And what were their names?

2. Who confirmed that 'the cook was a good cook, as cooks go; and as good cooks go, she went'?

3. Who was 'the golden dustman'?

4. Who were 'the Cat, the Rat, and Lovell our dog' who ruled 'all England under a hog'?

5. Who was quite a good butler as butlers go, even though a bit sloppy with the silver?

6. Which butler complained that the champagne in married employers' houses was inferior to that in the establishments of bachelors?

7. Who remarked, 'Servants should never be ill. We have quite enough illnesses without them adding to the symptoms'?

8. Which servant warned, 'Beware, my lord, of jealousy;
It is the green-eyed monster which doth mock
The meat it feeds on'?

9. 'The children were bathed and dressed by a big dog, whose kennel was kept in the nursery'. What was the name of this useful animal?

10. What was the name of Professor Henry Higgins's housekeeper?

SEX AND ALL THAT

'If all the girls attending it [the Yale Prom] were laid end to end, I wouldn't be at all surprised'

Dorothy Parker quoted in *While Rome Burns*
by ALEXANDER WOOLLCOTT

1. Who claimed, 'pornography is an attempt to insult sex, to do dirt on it'?

2. Name the two New Yorkers who wrote *Is Sex Necessary?*

3. Who opined that 'it doesn't matter what you do in the bedroom as long as you don't do it in the street and frighten the horses'?

4. Who wrote, 'Elspeth had so many men. Two of her sisters rode, so to speak, her discarded mounts'?

5. Which comic wrote that 'When she saw the sign "Members Only" she thought of him'?

6. Whose response on being picked up was, 'No, no girl . . . it won't do'?

7. Who had hue, glance, sympathy, note, but turned to harlotry?

8. Who reflected, 'How alike are the groans of love to those of the dying'?

9. Who claimed that 'older women are the best because they always think they may be doing it for the last time'?

10. From which novel is this taken? 'Prostitution gives her an opportunity to meet people. It provides fresh air and wholesome exercise, and it keeps her out of trouble'

SIN

**'The world's as ugly, ay, as sin,
And almost as delightful'**

FREDERICK LOCKER-LAMPSON
'The Jester's Plea'

1. Whose view of sin is this? 'Sin is behovely, but all shall be well, and all shall be well, and all manner of thing shall be well'

2. 'His sins were scarlet, but his books were read'. Who hoped this would be said of him after his death?

3. Who declared that he was 'a man more sinned against than sinning'?

4. Which novel was subtitled *The Modern Prometheus*?

5. Who claimed that 'the principle of procrastinated rape is said to be the ruling one in all the great bestsellers'?

6. In which novel is it claimed that 'it is a right to hate sin, but not to hate the sinner'?

7. Which composer stated that 'sin cannot be undone, only forgiven'?

8. Who decreed that 'there is but one thing more dangerous than sin – the murder of a man's sense of sin'?

9. Who claimed that 'all sins are attempts to fill voids'?

10. Who wrote, 'The only people who should really sin
Are the people who can sin with a grin'?

SLAVERY

'Not to stand high in the opinion of one's slaves was as humiliating a thing as could happen to a Southerner'

MARGARET MITCHELL
Gone with the Wind

1. What, according to William Pitt the Younger, was the creed of slaves?

2. Who remarked that 'in a consumer society there are inevitably two kinds of slaves: the prisoners of addiction and the prisoners of envy'?

3. Who bought the estate 'where my father and grandfather were slaves, where they weren't even allowed inside the kitchen'?

4. 'Even if the human products of these institutions were all geniuses, they would finally wreck any modern civilized country after maintaining themselves according to their own notions at the cost of the squalor and slavery of four-fifths of its inhabitants'. To whom does this refer?

5. Which famous American anti-slavery novel was first published as a serial in the *National Era*?

6. Who stated, 'There are no "white" or "coloured" signs on the foxholes or graveyards of battle'?

7. Which play offers the advice, 'Never fight fair with a stranger, boy. You'll never get out of the jungle that way'?

8. Which author said, 'It comes as a great shock around the age of five, six or seven . . . to see Gary Cooper killing off the Indians and, although you are rooting for Gary Cooper, that the Indians are you'?

9. Who stated, 'The slave clings to his chains and he must have them struck from him'?

10. Who defined a state of slavery as one 'in which a man does what he likes to do in his spare time and in his working time that which is required of him'?

SLOTH

'To spend too much time in studies is sloth'

FRANCIS BACON
'Of Studies'

1. Which dusty-featured creatures are 'by sloth on sorrow fathered'?

2. Who stated, 'All my good reading, you might say, was done in the toilet'?

3. Who remarked, on being told of the death of President Coolidge, 'How do they know'?

4. Who wrote,

'O England! full of sin, but most of sloth;
Spit out thy phlegm, and fill thy breast with glory'?

5. In which novel does one of the characters observe, 'I like work; it fascinates me. I can sit and look at it for hours'?

6. Who sent whom the following doctor's note: 'If you are idle, be not solitary; if you are solitary, be not idle'?

7. Which playwright spent half his days in bed waiting to write plays about waiting for an end to waiting?

8. What jumpy singer was invited to dance 'after a lazy summer'?

9. Which novel was concerned with the activities of the military class although its author accused them of enjoying 'a state of obligatory and unimpeachable idleness'?

10. Whose favourite activity was sitting around doing nothing in a briar patch?

SPORT

'Some people think that football is a matter of life and death. I don't like that attitude. I can assure them it's much more serious'

BILL SHANKLY – manager of Liverpool 1959–74

1. What sport does Frank Machin play in which novel?

2. Who wrote that football 'is not really played for the pleasure of kicking the ball about, but is a species of fighting'?

3. Who wrote, 'Pam, I adore you, Pam, you great big mountainous sports girl'?

4. Who said of himself, 'My writing is nothing, my boxing is everything'?

5. Who wrote that 'it is international sport that helps to kick the world downhill. Started by foolish athletes . . . it is supported today by the desire for political prestige and the interests involved in gate moneys'?

6. Who wrote that while 'many Continentals think life is a game, the English think cricket is a game'?

7. Who organized a game of croquet with hedgehogs instead of balls?

8. When did the blacksmith have to lean on the shoulder of the baker, only to be foiled by an American whose Christian name was Shakespeare?

9. Who was shot in the foot by a starting pistol during the school sports day?

10. Which player was 'too fast for them, going on meandering runs into midfield, spreading out passes with delicate prods across the mud, and when he was near the goal we could hear the delicate slap, slap, slap of his boots on the ground'?

SUFFERING

'"I weep for you," the Walrus said:
"I deeply sympathize."
With sobs and tears he sorted out
Those of the largest size'

LEWIS CARROLL
'The Walrus and the Carpenter'

1. What bit Karl Leon Forelock?

2. Who died, ill and exhausted, after an unsuccessful attempt at academic betterment?

3. Whose suffering is described in an account of one day?

4. Who wrote, 'About suffering they were never wrong,
The Old Masters'?

5. Who declared, on being refused by the lady of his choice, 'My life will be sour grapes and ashes without you'?

6. Whose damp souls sprouted despondently at area gates?

7. Who described himself as 'Ernie Haemorrhoid, the poor man's Pyle'?

8. Who claimed that 'deprivation is for me what daffodils were for Wordsworth'?

9. Who wrote of whom, 'Like Shelley and Baudelaire, it may

be said of him that he suffered, in his own person, the neurotic ills of an entire nation'?

10. Who complained, 'In my situation as Chancellor of the University of Oxford, I have been much exposed to authors'?

SUICIDES

'The thought of suicide is a great source of comfort: with it a calm passage is to be made across many a bad night'

FRIEDRICH NIETZSCHE

1. Who, after bequeathing his watch to his roommate Shreeve and cleaning his teeth, killed himself on 2 June 1910?

2. Who concluded that as 'guns aren't lawful; nooses give; gas smells awful; you might as well live'?

3. Who wrote these lines a week before committing suicide:
'The woman is perfected.
Her dead
Body wears the smile of accomplishment'?

4. Where did Willy Loman commit suicide?

5. Which TV quiz show champion dumbfounded his brother Buddy and sister Franny by committing suicide?

6. Which Romantic poet and playwright, on being told it was 'very extraordinary' that he had hanged himself, remarked,

'Indeed, sir, it is a *most extraordinary* thing that he should have hanged himself, be the subject of an inquest, and yet that he should at this moment be speaking to you'?

7. Who has claimed to be 'the only man in the world who cannot commit suicide'?

8. Who wrote, 'It's against the law to commit suicide in this town . . . although what the law can do to a guy who commits suicide I am never able to figure out'?

9. Who wrote that 'there are many who dare not kill themselves for fear of what the neighbours might say'?

10. Who claimed this: 'If I had the use of my body I would throw it out of the window'?

THEATRE

'All playwrights should be dead for three hundred years'

JOSEPH L. MANCIEWICZ
All About Eve

1. Whose first play, *The Man Who Had all the Luck*, closed after only four performances?

2. In which play did a character plead, 'Put me into something loose'?

3. Which playwright said of himself, 'My body has certainly wandered a good deal, but my mind has not wandered nearly enough'?

4. Of which play was it written, 'It was as though someone had dramatized the cooking of Sunday dinner'?

5. What is the connection between *The Hothouse* and *The Weaker Vessel*?

6. Who 'dressed himself up so nattily for his first audition that none of the people there took him for an actor'?

7. From which farce come the words, 'It would take a far more concentrated woman than Amanda to be unfaithful every five minutes'?

8. Which playwright disparaged Bernard Shaw with the words, 'He writes like a Pakistani who has learned English when he was twelve years old in order to become a chartered accountant'?

9. Who said, 'English plays are like their English puddings: nobody has any taste for them but themselves'?

10. Who wrote, 'A play should give you something to think about. When I see a play and understand it the first time, then I know it can't be much good'?

TITLES

'Each had his past shut in him like the leaves of a book known to him by heart, and his friends would only read the title'

VIRGINIA WOOLF
Jacob's Room

1. What is the Leepenny?

2. Which Graham Greene novel was called 'an entertainment' in Britain but 'a novel' in America?

3. Which book by Aldous Huxley took its title from a phrase in John Milton's *Samson Agonistes*?

4. To whom did Charles Dickens dedicate *Hard Times*?

5. Who was the Go-Between?

6. Tom Wolfe has used zany titles for many of his stories and novels. Can you provide the themes of the following: a) 'The Last American Hero' b) 'Mau-Mauing the Flak Catchers' c) 'Radical Chic'?

7. What did George have that Lucy wanted?

8. Who was Edmond Dantès?

9. Name the spy who came in from the cold.

10. Which novel has the alternative title, *Some Bells that Rang an Old Year Out and a New Year In*?

TRAGEDY

'The composition of a tragedy requires testicles'

VOLTAIRE

1. Who wrote, 'The bad end unhappily, the good unluckily. That is what tragedy means'?

2. Who claimed that to be in society 'is merely a bore. But to be out of it simply a tragedy'?

3. 'I'll make him a shroud, and he shall be buried in the garden'. What was the name of the deceased? What was he?

4. Who wrote, 'A prisoner has no sex. He is God's own eunuch'?

5. Which poet's wife committed suicide by tragically drowning herself in the Serpentine?

6. Who wrote that 'nor law, nor duty bade me fight,
Nor public man, nor angry crowds,
A lonely impulse of delight
Drove to this tumult in the clouds'?

7. Name the villain who attempts to help Sir Percival Glyde's misdeeds in *The Woman in White* by Wilkie Collins.

8. Which poet, and playwright, was killed by the Nationalists during the Spanish Civil War?

9. 'Her voice was ever soft,
Gentle and low, an excellent thing in woman'
Of which tragic heroine was this said?

10. 'The President of the Immortals . . . had ended his sport with Tess'. Where were her last moments of liberty?

TRANSPORT

'There are only two emotions in a plane. Boredom and terror'

ORSON WELLES quoted in the *Observer*

1. What were the names of the railway children?

2. Which double agent changed trains in 1935?

3. Jules Verne's *Around the World in Eighty Days* experienced great success when it was published in 1873, but can you name the titles of his earlier two novels?

4. Who declared that 'trains sum up all the fogs and the muddled misery of the nineteenth century. They constitute, in fact, slums on wheels'?

5. Who claimed in which novel that 'there is nothing more enticing, disenchanting and enslaving, than the life of the sea'?

6. 'In the watches of the night he is always fresh and bright'. Name this sentinel and his whereabouts.

7. Augustus Melmotte had a reputation as a leading financier, but what was the speculation that went disastrously wrong and caused him to commit suicide?

8. Which American consumer protectionist wrote a book entitled *Unsafe at any Speed*?

9. Who visited the great railway bazaar, and said that 'travel is glamorous only in retrospect'?

10. Who wrote about 'the Night Mail, crossing the Border,
Bringing the cheque and the postal order'?

TRAVEL

'To travel hopefully is a better thing than to arrive'

ROBERT LOUIS STEVENSON
Virginibus Puerisque

1. Which are the quietest places under the sun?

2. What does Robert Coover's Pinocchio go to Venice to do?

3. Where did Sal Paradise go?

4. 'For lust of knowing what should not be known,
We take the Golden Road to Samarkand'
Who is speaking, and who is his travelling companion?

5. 'A hard time we had of it.
At the end we preferred to travel all night,
Sleeping in snatches'
Who are these travellers?

6. Who sailed to America aboard the first Cunard steamship, the *Britannia*?

7. Who swooned when he came to Thebes?

8. Who took passage on the *Tankadere*?

9. Which two professors crossed flights across the Atlantic in which book?

10. Who claimed of whom that he had 'an experience of women which extends over many nations and three continents'?

VIOLENCE

'Better be killed than frightened to death'

R.S. Surtees
Mr Facey Romford's Hounds

1. Whose play states that 'it is possibie to disagree with someone about the ethics of non-violence without wanting to kick his teeth in'?

2. Who defined violence as being 'the repartee of the illiterate'?

3. Who advised that you 'remove your pants before resorting to violence'?

4. Who advised when 'someone puts his hand on you, send him to the cemetery'?

5. 'He must have known me had he seen me as he was wont to see me, for he was in the habit of flogging me constantly. Perhaps he did not recognize me by my face'. Who was the unfortunate victim?

6. Who knew 'that the essence of war is violence, and that moderation in war is imbecility'?

7. Whose play suggests that 'a bit of shooting takes your mind off your troubles – it makes you forget the cost of living'?

8. Who killed Cock Robin?

9. Who 'went out to Charing Cross, to see Major-general Harrison hanged, drawn, and quartered . . . he looking as cheerful as any man could do in that condition'?

10. 'I have never understood this liking for war. It panders to instincts already catered for within the scope of any respectable domestic establishment'. Which play is this taken from?

WAR

'As long as war is regarded as wicked, it will always have its fascination. When it is looked upon as vulgar, it will cease to be popular'

OSCAR WILDE
'The Critic as Artist'

1. Who stated that 'to jaw-jaw is always better than to war-war'?

2. By what name is Major Effingham better known?

3. Who was besieged at Laodicea?

4. 'The war-drum throbbed no longer' in whose view of the future?

5. Who was the scholarly pedant who was responsible for the conquest of Britain?

6. About whom did Winston Churchill make the following observation: 'In defeat unbeatable: in victory unbearable'?

7. Who asked, 'Why do you lie with your legs ungainly huddled,
And one arm bent across your sullen cold
Exhausted face'?

8. Which playwright's father, Dr Eugene Strausser, was killed in Singapore during the Second World War?

9. From which poem, by whom, is this taken?
'Age shall not weary them, nor the years condemn.
At the going down of the sun and in the morning
We will remember them'

10. Which overweight airman remarked, 'Guns will make us powerful; butter will only make us fat'?

WEALTH

'It is as easy to marry a rich woman as a poor woman'

WILLIAM MAKEPEACE THACKERAY
Vanity Fair

1. Who claimed that if he received hostile criticism he would 'cry all the way to the bank'?

2. In which novel is it stated that 'the rich hate signing cheques. Hence the success of the credit cards'?

3. Who commented that 'in an age of egalitarianism it is assumed that no-one should have very much more than anyone else unless he wins it in a football pool'?

4. Who said, 'I don't know how many millions I'm worth. If you can actually count your money you are not a really rich man'?

5. Who told Simpkin not to lose the last penny of fourpence?

6. Who wrote in a letter to whom that 'the love of money is the root of all evil'?

7. Who was Nick Carraway's romantic and destructive neighbour?

8. Who habitually asked salesmen, 'Do you sincerely want to be rich?'

9. Who stated, in which play, 'I am a Millionaire. That is my religion'?

10. Who was the source of Pip's unexpected wealth in *Great Expectations*?

WEAPONS

'Keep up your bright swords, for the dew will rust them'

WILLIAM SHAKESPEARE
Othello

1. In 'The Ballad of Reading Gaol' by Oscar Wilde what does a coward use to 'kill the thing he loves'?

2. Who recommended, in the writing of a crime novel, 'when in doubt have a man come through the door with a gun in his hand'?

3. Which poet asks his 'tan-faced children',

   'Have you your pistols? have you your sharp-edged axes?

4. Weapons were in plentiful supply at the tournament at Ashby

de la Zouch, but name John's two chief knights defeated by the unknown Richard Coeur de Lion.

5. The use of which weapon is rewarded by a life of solitude and misery?

6. Who wrote, and in which poem,

'I shot an arrow into the air,
It fell to earth, I knew not where'?

7. Who remarked, 'In this war, we know, books are weapons. And it is a part of your dedication always to make them weapons for man's freedom'?

8. Where is it written that 'whoso pulleth out this sword of this stone and anvil is rightwise King born of all England'?

9. Who wrote,

'And this you can see is the bolt. The purpose of this
Is to open the breech, as you see'?

10. Who recommended, 'Shoot all the bluejays you want, if you can hit 'em, but remember it's a sin to kill a mockingbird'?

WELL-KNOWN PHRASES

'And therefore never send to know for whom the bell tolls; it tolls for thee'

JOHN DONNE
'Meditation XVII'

Who said:

1. 'Tomorrow to fresh woods, and pastures new'

2. 'We have become a grandmother'

3. 'Ships that pass in the night, and speak each other in passing'

4. 'Religion is the opium of the people'

5. 'Whom God would destroy He first sends mad'

6. 'Brevity is the soul of wit'

7. 'Life ain't all beer and skittles, and more's the pity; but what's the odds, so long as you're happy?'

8. 'Mad, bad, and dangerous to know'

9. 'The moving toyshop of their heart'

10. 'All for one, one for all'

WISDOM

'The price of wisdom is above rubies'

THE BOOK OF JOB

1. Who advised whom, 'Neither a borrower nor a lender be'?

2. Who warned, 'Have nothing in your houses that you do not know to be useful or believe to be beautiful'?

3. Whom did Tom Wolfe describe as 'the most important thinker since Newton, Darwin, Freud, Einstein and Pavlov'?

4. Which modern historian declared that 'education . . . has produced a vast population able to read but unable to distinguish what is worth reading'?

5. Who wrote that 'one is not born a woman: one becomes one'?

6. Who remarked that 'the critical period in matrimony is breakfast-time'?

7. Who stated that 'long engagements . . . give people the opportunity of finding out each other's character before marriage, which I think is never advisable'?

8. Who claimed to be able to call spirits from the vasty deep?

9. 'None but the fools doubt the wisdom of the *Jupiter*; none but

the mad dispute its facts.' In whose life does this newspaper play an important role?

10. Whose unfailing wisdom was considered by his employer to be the result of eating a great deal of fish?

WIT AND WISECRACKS

'Want of wit is worse than want of wealth'

KELLY
Proverbs

1. Who defined a cynic as 'a man who knows the price of everything and the value of nothing'?

2. Of which wit was this remarked: 'If his face suggested an old boot it was undoubtedly hand-made'?

3. Who pointed out that 'there's a hell of a distance between wisecracking and wit. Wit has truth in it; wisecracking is simply callisthenics with words'?

4. Who commented, 'He spoke with a certain what-is-it in his voice, and I could see that, if not actually disgruntled, he was far from being gruntled'?

5. Who, when someone complained, 'That's bigamy', retorted, 'Yes, and it's big of me too'?

6. Who offered the definition that 'the plural of spouse is spice'?

7. Who claimed that 'English Humour resembles the Loch Ness Monster in that both are famous but there is a strong suspicion that neither of them exists'?

8. Who wrote this letter of complaint:
'Sir,
Saturday morning, although recurring at regular and well-overseen intervals, always seems to take this railway by surprise'?

9. In tackling fan mail, who had these words of advice: 'In case of impudent letters from married women I write to the husband warning him his wife is attempting to enter into correspondence with strange men'?

10. Who wrote, 'Being an old maid is like death by drowning, a really delightful sensation after you cease to struggle'?

ANSWERS

ACCESSORIES

1.a)Sydenstriller b)Seward c)Samuel. 2.Mae West 3.The infant Jack Worthing in *The Importance of Being Earnest* by Oscar Wilde 4.Bernard Clark to Alfred Salteena in *The Young Visiters* by Daisy Ashford 5.Belinda in 'The Rape of the Lock' by Alexander Pope 6.'I am' – 'Sergeant Brown's Parrot' by Kit Wright 7.Christopher Robin in 'Vespers' from *When We Were Very Young* by A.A. Milne 8.A.E. Housman in *The Name and Nature of Poetry* 9.Samuel Johnson 10.Touchstone in *As You Like It* by William Shakespeare

AFFAIRS

1.*Eyeless in Gaza* by Aldous Huxley 2.Ralph de Bricassart in *The Thorn Birds* by Colleen McCullough 3.*The Passion* by Jeanette Winterson 4.Dorothy Sayers in 'That's Why I Never Read Modern Novels' 5.William Shakespeare, 'Sonnet 138' 6.*More Than Somewhat* by Damon Runyon 7.*Sam and Prudence* by Barbara Pym 8.*Inside Mr Enderby* by Anthony Burgess 9.*Vile Bodies* by Evelyn Waugh 10.Holden Caulfield in *The Catcher in the Rye* by J.D. Salinger

ARISTOCRATS

1.Oxford in *Decline and Fall* by Evelyn Waugh 2.*The Viceroy of Ouidah* by Bruce Chatwin 3.'The Stately Homes of England', in the song from *Operette* by Noel Coward 4.John Collins Bossidy, speech quoted in *Springfield Sunday Republican* 5.Oscar Wilde of Frank Harris 6.Count Dracula's in *Dracula* by Bram Stoker 7.Lord Lucky in 'More Keys' by Hilaire Belloc 8.Benjamin Disraeli on his elevation to the House of Lords 9.Marco and Giuseppe from *The Gondoliers* by W.S. Gilbert 10.Giuseppe Tomasini, Principe di Lampedusa. The book describes the exploits of Prince Fabrizio in the 1860s

ART AND ARTISTS

1.Sir Edwin Landseer 2.Mr Pooter in *Diary of a Nobody* by George and Weedon Grossmith 3.J.A.D. Ingres 4.W.H. Auden in 'Letter to Lord Byron III' 5.Aldous Huxley in *Along the Road* 6.Gulley Jimson in *The Horse's Mouth* by Joyce Cary 7.William Hogarth 8.Vincent van Gogh; his ear 9.Thomas Gainsborough 10.Edgar Degas

AUTHORS

1.Mikhail Bulgakov, *The Master and Margarita* 2.Benjamin Disraeli 3.Malcolm Bradbury 4.W.B. Yeats 5.W.C. Sellar and R.J. Yeatman of Oscar Wilde in *1066 and All That* 6.Jane Austen 7.Cyril Connolly in *Enemies of Promise* 8.V.S. Naipaul 9.*David Copperfield* 10.George Borrow. In gypsy language, a philologist.

THE BARD

1.Shylock 2.Blunt in *Henry IV Part I* 3.Polonius in *Hamlet* 4.Mark Antony in *Antony and Cleopatra*; Cleopatra and his captains 5.Richard III 6.Richard II 7.Falstaff in *Henry V* 8.Imogen in *Cymbeline* 9.Sir Toby Belch in *Twelfth Night* 10.The Garter Inn, Windsor in *The Merry Wives of Windsor*

BIOGRAPHY

1.Frederick Rolfe (a.k.a. Baron Corvo), A.J.A. Symons 2.Hilaire Belloc, *Cautionary Tales* 3.H.G. Wells 4.Elizabeth Cleghorn Gaskell 5.Malcolm Muggeridge in *Tread Softly For You Tread On My Jokes* 6.Henry James quoted in *Henry James, The Master 1901-1916* 7.1791 8.John Aubrey, author of *Brief Lives* 9.Lord Byron, referring to the instantaneous success of 'Childe Harold's Pilgrimage' in the biography by Thomas Moore 10.Cardinal Manning, Florence Nightingale, Thomas Arnold and General Gordon.

BIRTH

1.The mother of Tristram Shandy in *Tristram Shandy* by Tobias Smollett 2.David Copperfield 3.The Magi in 'Journey of the Magi' by T.S. Eliot 4.Dorothy Parker 5.Falstaff in *King Henry IV Part 2* 6.The nightingale in 'Ode to a Nightingale' by John Keats 7.T.S. Eliot in 'Sweeney Agonistes, Fragment of an Agon' 8.*The Day of the Locust* by Nathaniel West 9.Adolphus Cusins, the fiancé of Barbara in *Major Barbara* by George Bernard Shaw 10.Thomas Hood in 'I Remember'

CARICATURES AND CARTOONS

1.Raphael (1483-1520) 2.James Gillray (1757-1815) 3.Hablot Knight Browne (1815-82) using the pseudonym of 'Phiz' 4.William Combe and the adventures of *Dr Syntax* 5.George Cruikshank (1792-1878) 6.David Hockney 7.Charles Keene 8.Ralph Steadman 9.Thomas Bewick 10.The Tailor of Gloucester in Beatrix Potter's *The Tailor of Gloucester*

CHILDREN

1.*The Water Babies* by Charles Kingsley 2.Captain Walker to his family in a telegram in *Swallows and Amazons* by Arthur Ransome 3.Mowgli in *The Jungle Book* by Rudyard Kipling 4.Mole and Ratty's in *The Wind in the Willows* by Kenneth Grahame 5.P.G. Wodehouse in *The Heart of a Goof* 6.Francis Bacon in *The Advancement of Learning* 7.Edmund and Peter, Lucy and Susan from *The Lion, The Witch and The Wardrobe* by C.S. Lewis 8.Their son, Albert, was eaten by a lion in 'The Lion and Albert' by Marriott Edgar 9.Quentin Crisp in *The Naked Civil Servant* 10.The Duchess in *Alice's Adventures in Wonderland* by Lewis Carroll; a pig

CINEMA

1.William Faulkner 2.Peter Ustinov to play Nero in *Quo Vadis*, as told in his memoirs *Dear Me* 3.*A Day at the Races* 4.*The Third Man* 5.Pier Paolo Pasolino, whose unfinished novel was entitled *Petralio* 6.Charlie Chaplin 7.Alfred Hitchcock 8.Errol Flynn, quoted in *Great Lovers of the Movies* 9.Humphrey Bogart in *Casablanca* 10.Samuel Goldwyn in an address at Balliol College, Oxford, March 1945

CRIME AND DETECTION

1.Charles Dickens's Martin Chuzzlewhit 2.*The Black Mask* 3.They are characters in the Wycliffe detective novels by W.J. Burley 4.*Decline and Fall* by Evelyn Waugh 5.Arsene Dupin 6.Brother Cadfael in novels by Ellis Peters 7.Agatha Christie 8.G.K. Chesterton, in his 'Father Brown' stories 9.Macbeth, by one of the three witches in *Macbeth* by William Shakespeare 10.Alice Brown, from *Bab Ballads*, 'Gentle Alice Brown' by W.S. Gilbert

DEATH

1.Mark Twain in *New York Journal*, 2 June 1897 2.The Thane of Cawdor in *Macbeth* by William Shakespeare 3.Canon Henry Scott Holland 4.Othello of Desdemona in *Othello* by William Shakespeare 5.Oscar Wilde of the scene in *The Old Curiosity Shop* by Charles Dickens 6.Conrad's Lord Jim 7.Ian Fleming's Dr No 8.Querry in *A Burnt-Out Case* by Graham Greene 9.*Sanditon* 10.Percy Bysshe Shelley, who drowned off Leghorn, 8 July 1822, from *Recollections of the Last Days of Shelley and Byron* by E.J. Trelawny

DIARIES

1.*The Collector* by John Fowles 2.Ten 3.The Hon. Gwendolen Fairfax in *The Importance of Being Earnest* by Oscar Wilde 4.Jane Somers: *The Diaries of Jane Somers* by Doris Lessing 5.E.M. Delafield in *Diary of a Provincial Lady* 6.Dorry Carr in *What Katy Did* by Susan Coolidge 7.Virginia Woolf in *The Common Reader* 8.Catherine Earnshaw in *Wuthering Heights* by Emily Brontë 9.Queen Victoria 10.Samuel Pepys, 1 May 1663

DIVORCE AND MARITAL INFIDELITY

1.Zsa Zsa Gabor 2.Eva Figes in *Patriarchal Attitudes* 3.William Carlos Williams in 'Paterson' 4.Edward Fawcett and Tony Thomas in *America, Americans* 5.*Private Lives* by Noel Coward 6.The poet John Milton in 1643 7.Cyril Connolly in *The Unquiet Grave* 8.Al Alvarez in *Life After Marriage* 9.Anna Wickham in 'Ship Near Shoals' 10.Charles Ryder and Julia Flyte in *Brideshead Revisited* by Evelyn Waugh

DREAMS

1.The unnamed narrator in the opening lines of *Rebecca* by Daphne du Maurier 2.Lord Byron in 'Don Juan' 3.The Duke of Clarence in *Richard III* by William Shakespeare 4.Evelyn Waugh in his *Diaries* 5.W.B. Yeats in 'He Wishes for the Cloths of Heaven' 6.T.E. Lawrence in *The Seven Pillars of Wisdom* 7.The Lord Chancellor in *Iolanthe* by W.S. Gilbert 8.Graham Greene in the *Sunday Times* 9.T.E. Lawrence in *Seven Pillars of Wisdom* 10.Dylan Thomas in *Under Milk Wood*

DRINK

1.Emma Woodhouse of Rev. Elton in *Emma* by Jane Austen 2.T.F. Powys 3.George Bernard Shaw's Major Barbara in *Major Barbara* 4.Paul the Apostle to Timothy 5.'The Lips That Touch Liquor Must Never Touch Mine' by George W. Young 6.Winston Churchill in *My Early Life* 7.Oscar Wilde 8.Miss Jenkyns and Miss Matty in *Cranford* by Mrs Gaskell 9.King Henry V in *Henry V* by William Shakespeare 10.Wine and women, from *The Anatomy of Melancholy*

ECCENTRICS AND EXTROVERTS

1.Sir Thomas Beecham, quoted in *The Great Conductors* 2.Howard Hughes in his last public statement 3.Dolores Ibarruri, Spanish Communist leader 4.Alan Coren in *The Sanity Inspector* 5.Liberace 6.Ernest Hemingway about Noel Coward, quoted in *Blessings in Disguise* 7.Frank Harris 8.Mrs Malaprop in *The Rivals* by Richard Brinsley Sheridan 9.The White Knight in *Through The Looking-Glass* by Lewis Carroll 10.A doctor

EDUCATION

1.New Carthage 2.Mary Wollstonecraft's Victor Frankenstein 3.Jilly Cooper 4.Gussie Fink-Nottle, since Jeeves has advised him that this might conquer his nervousness and make it easier to propose to Madeleine Bassett, in *Right Ho, Jeeves* by P.G. Wodehouse 5.Because of the similarity of prison life to an English public school – *Decline and Fall* by Evelyn Waugh 6.Wackford Squeers's Academy, Dotheboys Hall in *Nicholas Nickleby* by Charles Dickens 7.Magdalen College, Oxford in Edward Gibbon's *Autobiography* 8.Eton College, 'Ode on a Distant Prospect of Eton College' by Thomas Gray 9.Lewis Eliot, barrister 10.Bertrand Welch, whose father is a professor in the novel by Kingsley Amis

ENTERTAINMENTS

1.Sir Thomas Beecham 2.Young Tom Bertram and his sisters in *Mansfield Park* by Jane Austen 3.Katharine Whitehorn in *Sunday Best* 4.The Owl in 'The Owl and the Pussycat' by Edward Lear 5.Dorothy Parker 6.H.L. Mencken 7.Luigi Pirandello in *Each in his Own Way* 8.The players who visited Elsinore in *Hamlet* by William Shakespeare 9.Marcel Marceau in *Theatre Art Magazine* 10.Kenneth Tynan in *Curtains*

EPITAPHS, –GRAPHS AND –GRAMS

1.Dr Jonathan Swift in 'Verses on the Death of Dr Swift' 2.Somerset Maugham in *A Writer's Notebook* 3.W.B. Yeats. Drumcliff, Sligo 4.Italo Calvino 5.He was able to plead benefit of the clergy and instead was branded as a felon 6.Alexander Pope 7.Joaquim Maria Machado de Assis (1829–1908); the book first appeared in 1880 8.Friedrich Nietzsche 9.William Blake 10.Edmund Clerihew Bentley in *Biography for Beginners*

FAME

1.Francis Bacon in 'Of Praise' 2.John Milton in 'Lycidas' 3.Howard Spring 4.Ford Madox Ford 5.Richard Porson in *Facetiae Cantabrigienses* 6.J.M. Barrie in his Presidential Address to The Society of Authors, 1928 7.Lord Byron in 'Stanzas written on the road between Florence and Pisa' 8.Percy Bysshe Shelley in 'An Exhortation' 9.*Love's Labour's Lost* 10.Oscar Wilde

FAMILIES

1.*Anna Karenina* by Leo Tolstoy 2.Baldwin was Kipling's cousin and Burne-Jones was Kipling's uncle 3.Flora Poste in *Cold Comfort Farm* by Stella Gibbons 4.The Sitwells 5.Nicodemus in *Mr Midshipman Easy* by Frederick Marryat 6.Mother of Jo March and her sisters in *Little Women* by Louisa May Alcott 7.The Fossil family in *Ballet Shoes* by Noel Streatfeild 8.A preacher 9.The building trade. Old Jolyon's father was a master builder, Superior Dossett, as shown in *The Man of Property* by John Galsworthy 10.Mr Knightley to Emma Woodhouse in *Emma* by Jane Austen

FANTASY

1.They are in books by Terry Pratchett 2.*Flow My Tears The Policeman Said* by Philip K. Dick 3.The Jumblies in a poem by Edward Lear 4.The Snark in 'The Hunting of the Snark' by Lewis Carroll 5.Eight – two owls and a hen, four larks and a wren 6.Bilbo Baggins in *The Hobbit* by J.R.R. Tolkien 7.Mars in *The War of the Worlds* by H.G. Wells 8.They were the names of Aragorn, heir to Elendil and King of Arnor and Gondor in *The Lord of the Rings* by J.R.R. Tolkien 9.William Beckford's *Vathek* 10.Mars and Venus in *Out of the Silent Planet* and *Voyage to Venus* by C.S. Lewis

FIRST LINES

1.'Undertones of War' by Edmund Blunden 2.*The Good Soldier* by Ford Madox Ford 3.*The Moonstone* by Wilkie Collins 4.*David Copperfield* by Charles Dickens 5.*Pride and Prejudice* by Jane Austen 6.'Ozymandias' by Percy Bysshe Shelley 7.*Slaughterhouse Five* by Kurt Vonnegut 8.*Necromancer* by William Gibson 9.*Moby Dick* by Herman Melville 10.*The Towers of Trebizond* by Rose Macaulay

FOOD

1.Ben Gunn in *Treasure Island* by Robert Louis Stevenson 2.Tom Thumb and Hunca Munca in *The Tale of Two Bad Mice* by Beatrix Potter 3.*Scoop* by Evelyn Waugh 4.The March Hare in *Alice's Adventures in Wonderland* by Lewis Carroll 5.Edmund Clerihew Bentley of Edgar Allan Poe 6.Ernest Hemingway; Paris 7.From the Epistle Dedicatory to *Man and Superman* by George Bernard Shaw 8.D.H. Lawrence in *Sea and Sardinia* 9.Miss Isabel Poppit's in *Miss Mapp* by E.F. Benson 10.Norman Douglas in *Siren Land*

HATRED AND MURDER

1.Flay in *Titus Groan* by Mervyn Peake 2.Samuel Butler in *Notebooks* 3.Aldous Huxley in *Beyond the Mexique Bay* 4.Bertrand Russell 5.Huckleberry Finn in *The Adventures of Huckleberry Finn* by Mark Twain 6.Shylock of Antonio, *The Merchant of*

Venice by William Shakespeare 7.W.B. Yeats in 'A Prayer for My Daughter' 8.The Jabberwock in *Through the Looking-Glass* by Lewis Carroll 9.*Major Barbara* by George Bernard Shaw 10.Winston Churchill in *The Grand Alliance*

HEROISM

1.Horatio Nelson 2.Patrick White's Voss 3.Horatius in *Lays of Ancient Rome* by Lord Macaulay 4.a)Rabelais in 'The Last of the Stores' b)P.G. Wodehouse as told to Richard Usborne and c)Noel Coward in the biography by Cole Leslie 5.Alfred, Lord Tennyson 6.Raymond Chandler, describing his private eye in *Atlantic Monthly*, 'The Simple Art of Murder' 7.Ernest Hemingway in *Portrait of Hemingway* by Lillian Ross 8.Spike Milligan's Puckoon 9.T.S. Eliot in 'Gerontion' 10.*Beauchamp's Career* by George Meredith

HISTORY

1.D'Artagnan in *The Three Musketeers* by Alexandre Dumas 2.King Arthur, known as the Wart in T.H. White's trilogy *The Once and Future King* 3.Charles II, according to the Earl of Rochester 4.Jane Austen 5.Before the Battle of Waterloo according to 'Childe Harold's Pilgrimage' by Lord Byron 6.Thomas Hardy's poem 'Christmas: 1924' 7.Benjamin Disraeli to Queen Victoria in December 1874, suggesting Carlyle be given an honour 8.Thomas Babington Macaulay according to the biography by Sir G.O. Trevelyan 9.Henry Ford (1863-1947) in *Chicago Tribune*, May 1916 10.George Bernard Shaw in *The Revolutionist's Handbook*

HONS, REBELS AND OTHERS

1.David Niven, *Round the Rugged Rocks* 2.Daisy Ashford, author of *The Young Visiters* 3.Thomas Hardy 4.*Ultramarine*. The author is Malcolm Lowry 5.*Flaws in the Glass* (by Patrick White).

1973 6.Charles Lutwidge Dodgson (Lewis Carroll), lecturer in mathematics 7.James Morris and Jan Morris. They are the same person 8.Joe Orton 9.*I Live under a Black Sun* by Dame Edith Sitwell; the subject is Dean Swift 10.Lord Alfred Douglas; Oscar Wilde; *Salome*

HORSES

1.Lord Scamperdale in *Mr Sponge's Sporting Tour* by R.S. Surtees 2.John Florio in *Second Frutes* 3.Lord Ronald in 'Gertrude the Governess' by Stephen Leacock 4.Roland, the narrator's horse, who has been bringing the good news from Ghent to Aix, in the poem by Robert Browning 5.David Niven, Eric Williams, Horace McCoy 6.Sir Andrew Aguecheek in *Twelfth Night* by William Shakespeare 7.Meg in the poem by Robert Burns 8.The Traveller in 'The Listeners' by Walter de la Mare 9.Smudges in 'Hunter Trials' by John Betjeman 10.Sir Gawain

INSULTS AND ABUSE

1.Reverend Sydney Smith of Macaulay in the *Lady Holland Memoir* 2.Max Beerbohm in *The Yellow Book*, 'A Defence of Cosmetics' 3.F. Scott Fitzgerald quoted in *Some Sort of Grandeur* by Matthew J. Broccoli 4.Peter Fleming in the *Sunday Times* 5.Macbeth to a servant in *Macbeth* by William Shakespeare 6.*Pygmalion* by George Bernard Shaw 7.John Sparrow 8.Oscar Wilde on George Bernard Shaw 9.Lillian Hellman 10.*Chips with Everything* by Arnold Wesker

JEALOUSY

1.Othello in *Othello* by William Shakespeare 2.Françoise Sagan in *La Chamade* 3.Ralph Waldo Emerson, 'Wealth' 4.Captain Absolute and Bob Acres 5.Elizabeth Bowen in *The House in Paris* 6.The Song of Solomon in the Bible 7.John Gay in 'The Elephant and the Bookseller' 8.Havelock Ellis, *On Life and Sex*

9. *The Stand-In* by Deborah Moggach 10. Gertrude in *Hamlet* by William Shakespeare

JUSTICE

1. Titus Andronicus in the play of that name by William Shakespeare 2. *Anna Karenina* by Leo Tolstoy 3. Kent to the King in *King Lear* by William Shakespeare 4. Hester Prynne in *The Scarlet Letter* by Nathaniel Hawthorne 5. *The Fair Maid of Perth*, taken from Jedburgh, the border town where troopers were given this type of treatment 6. Mr Bumble in *Oliver Twist* 7. Arnold Bennett in *Things That Have Interested Me* 8. *The Rebel* by Albert Camus 9. *A Voyage Round My Father* by John Mortimer 10. The Mouse to Alice in *Alice's Adventures in Wonderland* by Lewis Carroll

LAST LINES AND WORDS

1. *The Great Gatsby* by F. Scott Fitzgerald 2. *Wuthering Heights* by Emily Brontë 3. The way the world ends in 'The Hollow Men' by T.S. Eliot 4. *A Portrait of the Artist as a Young Man* by James Joyce 5. *The Picture of Dorian Gray* by Oscar Wilde 6. *The Trial* by Franz Kafka 7. Thomas Gainsborough, quoted in the biography by William B. Boulton 8. Charles James Fox 9. *The Handmaid's Tale* by Margaret Atwood 10. Katherine Mansfield

LEADERSHIP

1. Maxim Gorky 2. Casterbridge in *The Mayor of Casterbridge* by Thomas Hardy 3. Eva Perón in *Evita* 4. Winston Churchill in *My Early Life* 5. A prince in *The Prince* by Niccolò Machiavelli 6. Horatius in *Lays of Ancient Rome* by Lord Macaulay 7. Alexander Chase in *Perspectives* 8. Groucho Marx in *News Review* 9. Thomas Macaulay referring to Sir Robert Peel 10. President Harry S. Truman in *Mr Citizen* (attributed to Harry Vaughan)

LETTERS

1.Saul Bellow's Herzog 2.Correspondence between Evelyn Waugh and Lady Diana Cooper who used these names most frequently in their letters between 1932 and 1966 3.W.H. Auden in 'Night Mail' 4.Mr Darcy to Elizabeth Bennet in *Pride and Prejudice* by Jane Austen 5.Samuel Johnson to the Earl of Chesterfield 6.Thomas Babington Macaulay 7.The Earl of Chesterfield, 1 April 1748 8.Mrs M'Lehose and Robbie Burns 9.D.H. Lawrence 10.Lewis Carroll

LIES AND TRUTHS

1.Holden Caulfield in *The Catcher in the Rye* by J.D. Salinger 2.Huckleberry Finn in *The Adventures of Huckleberry Finn* by Mark Twain 3.Benjamin Disraeli 4.Patrick White in *Flaws in the Glass* 5.Somerset Maugham in *The Constant Wife* 6.Matilda in *Cautionary Tales* by Hilaire Belloc 7.Topsy in *Uncle Tom's Cabin* by Harriet Beecher Stowe 8.*Heartbreak House* by George Bernard Shaw 9.Alexander Solzhenitsyn in *Candle in the Wind* 10.Touchstone in *As You Like It* by William Shakespeare

LOCALES

1.Greenwich Village 2.Britain in *1984* by George Orwell 3.Peckham, in *The Ballad of Peckham Rye* by Muriel Spark 4.Inside the Caves of Marabar in *A Passage to India* by E.M. Forster 5.James Woodforde, 1740-1803, who kept a celebrated *Diary* 6.New York. *New York Trilogy* by Paul Auster 7.The Floss. *The Mill on the Floss* by George Eliot 8.Sir Arthur Conan Doyle in *A Study in Scarlet* 9.Paris. If bad they are returned to America 10.The pilgrimage in *The Canterbury Tales* by Geoffrey Chaucer

LOVE

1.Mr Cheeseacre and Captain Bellfield, who became the lucky

man. From *Can You Forgive Her?* by Anthony Trollope 2.W.H. Auden in 'September 1, 1939' 3.St Augustine of Hippo 4.Fainall in *The Way of the World* by William Congreve 5.The narrator and Annabel Lee in the poem 'Annabel Lee' by Edgar Allan Poe 6.'She such a very ordinary little woman: he such a thumping crook'. From 'In A Bath Teashop' by John Betjeman 7.Rosalind in *As You Like It* by William Shakespeare 8.Lucia from the Mapp and Lucia novels by E.F. Benson 9.Absence 10.John Wesley. From *Life of Wesley* by R. Southey

LUST AND CHASTITY

1.Charles Smithson in *The French Lieutenant's Woman* by John Fowles 2.John Berry in *The Hotel New Hampshire* by John Irving 3.John Ford's *'Tis Pity She's a Whore* in which both Giovanni and the sister he has impregnated, Annabella, finish dead 4.Nicholas 5.*Les Liaisons Dangereuses* by Pierre Choderlos de Laclos 6.Jay Gatsby's in *The Great Gatsby* by F. Scott Fitzgerald 7.Jimmy Carter quoted in *Playboy*, November 1976 8.John Betjeman in 'Senex' 9.Philip Larkin, 'Letter to a Friend about Girls' 10.In a marble vault. 'To his Coy Mistress' by Andrew Marvell

MARRIAGE

1.John Gilpin in the poem by William Cowper 2.Flora in *The Soul of Kindness* by Elizabeth Taylor 3.Rev. Sydney Smith 4.Mrs Patrick Campbell quoted in *While Rome Burns* by Alexander Woollcott 5.John Clare, 'Child Harold' 6.He was twelve years her junior 7.Dorothea Brooke in *Middlemarch* by George Eliot 8.Hereward the Wake in the poem by Charles Kingsley 9.Jane Eyre married Edward Rochester in *Jane Eyre* by Charlotte Brontë 10.Charlotte Lucas in *Pride and Prejudice* by Jane Austen

MEDLEY

1.Richard Hannay in *The Thirty-Nine Steps* by John Buchan 2.Dorothy Parker 3.Peter Fleming in *One's Company* 4.George Cruikshank 5.Don Quixote in the novel of the same name by Miguel de Cervantes 6.Yram 7.Lord Acton 8.Lord Kenneth Clark in *Civilisation* 9.Salvador Dali in *Conquest of the Irrational* 10.Alan Bennett in *Beyond the Fringe*

MEMOIRS AND SELF-PORTRAITS

1.James Joyce in *A Portrait of the Artist as a Young Man* 2.Edward Gibbon 3.Norman Lewis, described in *Jackdaw Cake* 4.Siegfried Sassoon 5.Rudyard Kipling 6.Beverley Nichols, *Twenty-five* 7.Henri Philippe Pétain (1856–1951) 8.The Duc de Saint-Simon (1675–1755) 9.*Memoirs of A Woman of Pleasure* by John Cleland 10.V.S. Naipaul in *Such A Strange Lady* by Janet Hitchman

MUSIC

1.*Clea* by Lawrence Durrell 2.God in the poem 'Stradivarius' by George Eliot 3.Rev. Rowland Hill, in the biography by E.W. Broome 4.*The Mourning Bride* by William Congreve 5.Sir Ernest Newman about Igor Stravinsky in *Musical Times* 6.Pablo Casals 7.Yehudi Menuhin in *Theme and Variations* 8.Quentin Crisp in *Manners from Heaven* 9.Gustav Mahler as told in the biography by Blankopf 10.Mozart and Salieri in *Outline of Russian Literature*

ODDMENTS

1.Tristram Shandy 2.Rev. William Spooner, in the biography by William Hayter 3.Francis Bacon, 'Of Death' 4.Ogden Nash, 'Family Correct' 5.*Ulysses* by James Joyce 6.Oscar Wilde 7.*Brave New World* by Aldous Huxley 8.Katherine Mansfield, who died of tuberculosis in the Gurdjieff community in Fontainebleau in

1935 9.The Hunter of the East in *The Rubáiyát of Omar Khayyám* by Edward Fitzgerald 10.John Milton, *Paradise Lost*

ODD ONE OUT

1.Mario Vargas Llosa is Peruvian, the other three Colombian 2.Smeagol, who is a character from *The Lord of the Rings*. All the others were visited by Jonathan Swift's Gulliver on his travels. 3.Robert Lowell is the only one not born in Lowell, Massachusetts 4.Father Merrill is from *A Prayer for Owen Meany* by John Irving, the others are characters from *Catch-22* by Joseph Heller 5.*The Small House at Allington* is by Anthony Trollope, the others by Charles Dickens 6.They were all wives of Ernest Hemingway apart from Lillian Hellman 7.Adam Dalgliesh is a professional detective, the others are amateurs 8.Hare appears in the Little Grey Rabbit books by Alison Uttley; the others appear in *The Wind in the Willows* by Kenneth Grahame 9.Mr Lovelace appears in Samuel Richardson's *Clarissa*, the rest are heroes in Jane Austen's novels 10.*The Sound and the Fury* is by William Faulkner. All the others are by F. Scott Fitzgerald

OLD AGE

1.Father William in *Alice's Adventures in Wonderland* by Lewis Carroll 2.King Lear, William Shakespeare 3.J. Alfred Prufrock in 'The Love Song of J. Alfred Prufrock' by T.S. Eliot 4.W.B. Yeats in 'Sailing to Byzantium' 5.Grantchester people in 'The Old Vicarage, Grantchester' by Rupert Brooke 6.Miss Havisham in *Great Expectations* by Charles Dickens 7.Uncle Arly from 'Incidents in the life of Uncle Arly' by Edward Lear 8.Percy Bysshe Shelley on George III in 'Sonnet: England in 1819' 9.Mr Salteena in *The Young Visiters* by Daisy Ashford 10.Jonathan Swift in *Thoughts on Various Subjects*

OPTIMISM AND PESSIMISM

1.John Kennedy Toole committed suicide in 1980 because the novel had been rejected by every publisher who'd seen it. 2.Max Beerbohm in *And Even Now* 3.Samuel Johnson in James Boswell's *Life* 4.Arnold Bennett in *Things That Have Interested Me* 5.Cecil Rhodes 6.Mr Micawber in *David Copperfield* by Charles Dickens 7.King George IV on seeing Caroline of Brunswick, as told in the diaries of the Earl of Malmesbury 8.Antoine de Saint-Exupéry in *Wind, Sand and Stars* 9.Laurence Peter in *Peter's Quotations* 10.W.C. Fields as quoted in *The Times Literary Supplement*

PETS

1.Virginia Woolf. Flush 2.'Cats' by A.S. Tessimond 3.Holden Caulfield in *The Catcher in the Rye* by J.D. Salinger 4.A.L. Rowse in *Three Cornish Cats* 5.A python, 'The Python' by Hilaire Belloc 6.Thomas Gray in 'Ode on the Death of a Favourite Cat' 7.A bullfinch who was killed by a rat in 'On the Death of Mrs Throckmorton's Bulfinch' (sic) by William Cowper 8.Dr Samuel Johnson in Boswell's *Life of Samuel Johnson*, Edward Lear (preface to *Nonsense Songs*) and Christopher Smart in *Jubilate Agno* 9.Dorothy Parker, told in *While Rome Burns* by Alexander Woollcott 10.*Rogue Male* by Geoffrey Household

PLACES

1.Jorge Luis Borges in *Labyrinths* 2.*Tales of the City* by Armistead Maupin 3.Cedric Carol, Lord Fauntleroy in *Little Lord Fauntleroy* by Frances Hodgson Burnett 4.*Oliver Twist* by Charles Dickens 5.Amherst, Massachusetts 6.Silas Marner in the novel of the same name by George Eliot 7.The Dashwoods in *Sense and Sensibility* by Jane Austen 8.Richmond, Surrey 9.G.K. Chesterton in 'The Rolling English Road' 10.A Roman soldier in 'Roman Wall Blues' by W.H. Auden

POETRY AND POETS

1.Irina Ratushinskaya 2.W.H. Auden of W.B. Yeats 3.T.S. Eliot in *The Use of Poetry and the Use of Criticism* 4.Robert Burns in 'Epistle to James Smith' 5.They will be a dark patch upon the earth, from *Hassan* 6. Edward Bulwer Lytton 7.Percy Bysshe Shelley in his *Defence of Poetry* 8.Cyril Connolly in *Enemies of Promise* 9.William Wordsworth in the Preface to *Lyrical Ballads* 10.A.P. Herbert, 'Lines for a Worldly Person' in *Punch*

POLITICS

1.Rubashov in *Darkness at Noon* by Arthur Koestler 2.*Barnaby Rudge* by Charles Dickens 3.Malcolm Muggeridge in *Tread Softly For You Tread on My Jokes* 4.e.e. cummings 5.Senator Gotobed in *The American Senator* by Anthony Trollope 6.William Pitt 7.'The Unknown Citizen' by W.H. Auden 8.The Blackshorts – *The Code of the Woosters* by P.G. Wodehouse 9.George Orwell as described in *Homage to Catalonia* 10.*The King* by Donald Barthelme

POVERTY

1.E.M. Forster in *Howard's End* 2.Dylan Thomas 3.Jean Anouilh 4.'In days of old' according to Lord Macaulay in *Lays of Ancient Rome* 5.Uriah Heep in *David Copperfield* by Charles Dickens 6.Desdemona in *Othello* by William Shakespeare 7.John Keats in 'Ego Dominus Tuus' by W.B. Yeats 8.Doolittle in *Pygmalion* by George Bernard Shaw 9.*A Dandy in Aspic* by Derek Marlowe 10.Percy Bysshe Shelley to William Wordsworth in 'To Wordsworth'

PROFESSIONS

1.Jane Eyre in the novel of the same name by Charlotte Brontë 2.A doctor – Dr Dick Diver in *Tender is the Night* by F. Scott

Fitzgerald 3.Brynmor Jones Library, University of Hull 4.A novelist – *Earthly Powers* by Anthony Burgess 5.Jean Brodie in *The Prime of Miss Jean Brodie* by Muriel Spark 6.A high-class prostitute in *Mrs Warren's Profession* by George Bernard Shaw 7.He was trying to compile The Key to all Mythologies – *Middlemarch* by George Eliot 8.Margaret Hale in *North and South* by Elizabeth Gaskell 9.Anthony Trollope 10.Oscar Wilde in a letter to *St James's Gazette*

PSEUDONYMS

1.Albert Otto Max Feige who wrote as B. Traven 2.Eric Arthur Blair (1903-1950) 3.They are films of actor-writer-director Woody Allen né Konigsberg 4.Currer, Acton and Ellis Bell 5.Peter Collinson. Frequently both names would appear in the same issue of *Black Mask* 6.Mary Challans who wrote under the name of Mary Renault 7.Josephine Tey 8.Samuel Langhorne Clemens writing as Mark Twain 9.Palinurus, the drowned pilot of the *Aeneid* 10.John le Carré

REALISM

1.A highly-paid factory worker in Alan Sillitoe's novel 2.*Slaughterhouse Five* by Kurt Vonnegut 3.1948, twenty-five 4.D.H. Lawrence 5.*Portnoy's Complaint* by Philip Roth 6.Nicholas Jenkins 7.'Coming Through the Rye' by Robbie Burns; the novel is *The Catcher in the Rye* by J.D. Salinger 8.*Fanny's First Play* by George Bernard Shaw 9.Oscar Wilde in *The Picture of Dorian Gray* 10.*The Unquiet Grave* by Cyril Connolly

RELIGION

1.Mr Crisparkle in *The Mystery of Edwin Drood* by Charles Dickens 2.Louis MacNeice in 'Bagpipe Music' 3.God, according to Ronald Knox 4.a)Joanna Trollope b)E.H. Young c)Mrs Oliphant and d)Anthony Trollope 5.L. Ron Hubbard, at a science-fiction convention in New Jersey 6.Brendan Behan 7.Aldous Huxley in *Eyeless in Gaza* 8.Sydney Smith 9.John Wesley 10.Lord Macaulay

REMARKS

1.President John Kennedy at his Inaugural Address in Washington on 20 January 1961, reworking a phrase first used at the funeral of John Whittier in 1892 2.Cecil Beaton about Evelyn Waugh 3.In Samuel Johnson's *The Vanity of Human Wishes*; it implies from one end of the world to the other 4.Benjamin Franklin's in 'The Pessimist' 5.Joseph Hobson Jagger who in 1886 won over 2,000,000 francs in eight days. An expert on spindles, he suspected one of the roulette wheels of being faulty, and staked his money on the numbers that turned up most regularly 6.*Trilby* by George du Maurier 7.James McNeill Whistler, quoted in *Oscar Wilde* by Richard Ellman 8.The Duke of Wellington 9.The Duke of Gloucester, on being presented by Edward Gibbon with the second volume of *The Decline and Fall of the Roman Empire* 10.Marshal Foch

THE SEA

1.Wellingborough Redburn in *Redburn* by Herman Melville 2.Wolf Larsen in *The Sea-Wolf* by Jack London 3.William Golding's *To the Ends of the Earth: A Sea Trilogy* comprising *Rites of Passage, Close Quarters* and *Fire Down Below* 4.Squire Trelawney in *Treasure Island* by R.L. Stevenson 5.Captain Corcoran in *HMS Pinafore* by Gilbert and Sullivan 6.Ariel to Ferdinand in *The Tempest* by William Shakespeare 7.Captain Ahab in *Moby-Dick* by Herman Melville 8.Lord Byron in 'Childe Harold's Pilgrimage' 9.Dylan Thomas in *Under Milk Wood* 10.DEATH and LIFE-IN-DEATH in 'The Rime of the Ancient Mariner' by Samuel Taylor Coleridge

SERVANTS

1.Rudyard Kipling, 'I keep six honest serving-men'. What and Why and When and How and Where and Who, *Just So Stories* 2.'Saki' (H.H. Munro) in 'Reginald on Besetting Sins' 3.Mr Boffin in *Our Mutual Friend* by Charles Dickens 4.Sir William Catesby (d. 1485), Sir Richard Ratcliffe (killed at Bosworth in 1485), and Francis, Viscount Lovell (1454-?88) whose crest was a dog; the hog refers to the boar on Richard III's coat of arms. William Collingbourne, landowner and conspirator against Richard III. 5.Fred Crestwell in *Relative Values* by Noel Coward 6.Lane in *The Importance of Being Earnest* by Oscar Wilde 7.Lady Diana Cooper, quoted in the biography by Philip Ziegler 8.Iago to Othello in *Othello* by William Shakespeare 9.Nana in *The Story of Peter Pan* retold from J.M. Barrie's play by Daniel O'Connor 10.Mrs Pearce in *Pygmalion* by George Bernard Shaw

SEX AND ALL THAT

1.D.H. Lawrence 2.E.B. White and James Thurber 3.Mrs Patrick Campbell, quoted in *The Duchess of Jermyn Street* by Daphne Fielding 4.F. Scott Fitzgerald in *The Crack-Up and other Stories* 5.Spike Milligan, *Puckoon* 6.Samuel Johnson 7.Seraphina in 'Report on Experience' by Edmund Blunden 8.British Consul Geoffrey Firmin in Malcolm Lowry's *Under the Volcano* 9.Ian Fleming, quoted in *The Life of Ian Fleming* by John Pearson 10.*Catch-22* by Joseph Heller

SIN

1.Dame Julian of Norwich in *Revelations of Divine Love* 2.Hilaire Belloc, 'On His Books' 3.King Lear in *King Lear* by William Shakespeare 4.*Frankenstein* by Mary Shelley 5.V.S. Pritchett in *The Living Novel* 6.*The Little World of Don Camillo* by Giovanni Guareschi 7.Igor Stravinsky in *Conversations with Stravinsky* 8.Pope John Paul II in the *Observer*, April 1979 9.W.H. Auden in *A Certain World* 10.Ogden Nash in 'I'm A Stranger Here'

SLAVERY

1.Necessity. House of Commons, November 1783 2.Ivan Illich in *Tools for Conviviality* 3.Lopakhin in *The Cherry Orchard* by Anton Chekhov 4.The governing classes of England according to George Bernard Shaw in his introductory essay to *The Way of All Flesh* by Samuel Butler 5.*Uncle Tom's Cabin* by Harriet Beecher Stowe 6.President John Kennedy in his Message to Congress on proposed Civil Rights Bill, June 1963 7.*Death of a Salesman* by Arthur Miller 8.James Baldwin at the Cambridge Union, February 1965 9.Mahatma Gandhi in *Confessions of an Optimist* by Woodrow Wyatt 10.Eric Gill in 'Slavery and Freedom'

SLOTH

1.Lollocks in 'Lollocks' by Robert Graves 2.Henry Miller in 'Paris and its Suburbs' 3.Dorothy Parker 4.George Herbert in 'The Church Porch' 5.*Three Men in a Boat* by Jerome K. Jerome 6.Dr Samuel Johnson to James Boswell 7.Samuel Beckett 8.The Ant in 'The Ant and the Grasshopper' by Jean de la Fontaine 9.*War and Peace* by Leo Tolstoy 10.Brer Rabbit

SPORT

1.Rugby League. He's the protagonist in *This Sporting Life* by David Storey 2.George Orwell in 'Such, Such Were the Joys' 3.Sir John Betjeman in 'Pot Pourri from a Surrey Garden' 4.Ernest Hemingway 5.E.M. Forster in *Two Cheers for Democracy* 6.George Mikes in *How to be an Alien* 7.The Queen of Hearts in *Alice's Adventures in Wonderland* by Lewis Carroll 8.He'd sprained an ankle in a fall after bowling for Fordenden Cricket Club in A.G. MacDonell's *England, Their England* and was using the baker as a runner since he was the last man in. He was caught by Mr Shakespeare Pollock, and the match ended as a tie 9.Lord Tangent in *Decline and Fall* by Evelyn Waugh 10.Stanley Matthews, taken from *The Soccer Syndrome* by John Moynihan

SUFFERING

1.A redback spider in *Redback* by Howard Jacobson 2.Thomas Hardy's Jude the Obscure 3.*One Day in the Life of Ivan Denisovich* by Alexander Solzhenitsyn 4.W.H. Auden in 'Musée des Beaux Arts' 5.Alfred Salteena in *The Young Visiters* by Daisy Ashford 6.Housemaids', in 'Morning at the Window' by T.S. Eliot 7.Ernest Hemingway 8.Philip Larkin in *Required Writing* 9.Christopher Isherwood of T.E. Lawrence in *Exhumations* 10.The Duke of Wellington in *Recollections*

SUICIDES

1.Quentin Compson in *The Sound and the Fury* by William Faulkner 2.Dorothy Parker in 'Résumé' 3.Sylvia Plath in 'Edge' 4.In his car in *Death of a Salesman* by Arthur Miller 5.Seymour Glass in *Seymour: an Introduction* by J.D. Salinger 6.Samuel Taylor Coleridge only days after the opening of *Remorse* in 1813 7.Rev. Chad Varah, founder of the Samaritans 8.Damon Runyon in *Guys and Dolls* 9.Cyril Connolly in *The Unquiet Grave* 10.Samuel Beckett in *Malone Dies*

THEATRE

1.Arthur Miller's 2.*The Gay Lord Quex* by Sir Arthur Wing Pinero 3.Noel Coward 4.*A Doll's House* by Henrik Ibsen, reviewed in *Sporting and Dramatic News*, 1899 5.Harold Pinter wrote the former, Antonia Fraser the latter, and they are married 6.Marlon Brando, quoted in the *Sunday Express*, 16 July 1964 7.*Private Lives* by Noel Coward 8.John Osborne 9.Voltaire 10.T.S. Eliot in the *New York Post*, 1963

TITLES

1.The Talisman of the title by Sir Walter Scott 2.*Brighton Rock* 3.*Eyeless in Gaza* 4.Thomas Carlyle 5.Leo Colston in *The*

Go-Between by L.P. Hartley 6.a)Junior Johnson, a stock-car racer b)ensuring that those on the poverty program received their entitlements c)the espousal by wealthy New Yorkers of fashionable political movements such as the Black Panthers – 'I've never met a Panther – this is a first for me!' 7.A room with a view from the novel of that name by E.M. Forster 8.He became the Count of Monte Cristo in the novel of that title by Alexandre Dumas 9.Alec Leamas in *The Spy Who Came in from the Cold* by John le Carré 10.*The Chimes* by Charles Dickens

TRAGEDY

1.Tom Stoppard, *Rosencrantz and Guildenstern are Dead* 2.Lord Illingworth in *A Woman of No Importance* by Oscar Wilde 3.Pip, a canary in *Little Women* by Louisa M. Alcott 4.Henry Miller, *The Air-Conditioned Nightmare* 5.Percy Bysshe Shelley's wife, Harriet Westbrook 6.W.B. Yeats – 'An Irish Airman Foresees his Death' 7.Count Fosco 8.Federico García Lorca 9.Cordelia in *King Lear* by William Shakespeare 10.At Stonehenge in *Tess of the D'Urbervilles* by Thomas Hardy

TRANSPORT

1.Roberta known as Bobbie, Phyllis and Peter in *The Railway Children* by E. Nesbit 2.Arthur Norris in *Mr Norris Changes Trains* by Christopher Isherwood 3.*Journey to the Centre of the Earth* (1864) and *Twenty Thousand Leagues under the Sea* (1869) 4.Osbert Sitwell in 'Penny Foolish' 5.Joseph Conrad in *Lord Jim* 6.Skimbleshanks the Railway Cat on the Midnight Mail from *Old Possum's Book of Practical Cats* by T.S. Eliot 7.The Central American Railway in *The Way We Live Now* by Anthony Trollope 8.Ralph Nader 9.Paul Theroux 10.W.H. Auden in 'Night Mail'

TRAVEL

1.Clunton and Clunbury, Clungunford and Clun in A.E. Housman's *A Shropshire Lad*, no.50 2.To die 3.Colorado, California, Virginia, New York and Mexico in *On The Road* by Jack Kerouac 4.Ishak, Hassan. *Hassan* by James Elroy Flecker 5.The Magi in 'Journey of the Magi' by T.S. Eliot 6.Charles Dickens, *American Notes* 7.Arcite in *The Knight's Tale* by Geoffrey Chaucer 8.Phileas Fogg in 'Around the World in Eighty Days' by Jules Verne 9.Philip Swallow and Morris Zapp in *Changing Places* by David Lodge 10.Dr Watson of Sherlock Holmes in *The Sign of Four* by Arthur Conan Doyle

VIOLENCE

1.Christopher Hampton, *Treats* 2.Alan Brien in *Punch* 3.Yoko Ono, quoted in *The Pendulum Years* by Bernard Levin 4.Malcolm X in *Malcolm X Speaks* 5.Anthony Trollope from his *Autobiography* 6.John Hampden in 'John Hampden' by Lord Macaulay 7.Brendan Behan, *The Hostage* 8.I, said the Sparrow, with my bow and arrow – *Tommy Thumb's Pretty Song Book*, c.1744 9.Samuel Pepys, told in his *Diary*, 13 October 1660 10.*Forty Years On* by Alan Bennett

WAR

1.Winston Churchill in a speech at the White House, 26 June 1954 2.Hawkeye in *The Last of the Mohicans* by James Fenimore Cooper 3.Dolabella in *Antony and Cleopatra* by William Shakespeare 4.Alfred, Lord Tennyson's – 'Locksley Hall' 5.Claudius in *I, Claudius* by Robert Graves 6.Field-Marshal Montgomery 7.Siegfried Sassoon in 'The Dug-Out' 8.Tom Stoppard 9.'For the Fallen' (1914) by Laurence Binyon 10.Hermann Goering

WEALTH

1.Wladziu Valentino Liberace in his *Autobiography* 2.*Dr Fischer of Geneva* by Graham Greene 3.William Davis in *No Sin to be Rich* 4.Paul Getty, quoted in *The Pendulum Years* by Bernard Levin 5.The Tailor of Gloucester in the story of the same name by Beatrix Potter 6.St Paul in his first epistle to Timothy, from the Bible 7.Jay Gatsby in *The Great Gatsby* by F. Scott Fitzgerald 8.Bernard Cornfeld, American businessman 9.Andrew Undershaft in *Major Barbara* by George Bernard Shaw 10.Abel Magwitch, the convict, in the novel by Charles Dickens

WEAPONS

1.A kiss 2.Raymond Chandler in *Atlantic Monthly*, 'The Simple Art of Murder' 3.Walt Whitman in 'Pioneers! O Pioneers!' 4.The Templars Brian de Bois-Guilbert and Sir Reginald Front-de-Boeuf in *Ivanhoe* by Sir Walter Scott 5.The cross-bow used by the ancient mariner to kill the albatross in 'The Rime of the Ancient Mariner' by Samuel Taylor Coleridge 6.Henry Wadsworth Longfellow in 'The Arrow and the Song' 7.Franklin Delano Roosevelt in 'Message to the Booksellers of America', May 1942 8.*Le Morte D'Arthur* by Sir Thomas Malory 9.Henry Reed in 'Lessons of the War: 1, Naming of Parts' 10.Atticus Finch in *To Kill a Mockingbird* by Harper Lee

WELL-KNOWN PHRASES

1.John Milton, 'Lycidas' 2.Baroness Thatcher 3.Henry Wadsworth Longfellow, 'The Theologian's Tale' 4.Karl Marx in the introduction to *The Critique of Hegel's Philosophy of Right* 5.James Duport, *Homeri Gnomologia* 6.William Shakespeare, *Hamlet* 7.George du Maurier, *Trilby* 8.Lady Caroline Lamb, of Lord Byron 9.Alexander Pope in 'The Rape of the Lock' 10.The Three Musketeers in *The Three Musketeers* by Alexandre Dumas

WISDOM

1.Polonius to Laertes in *Hamlet* by William Shakespeare 2.William Morris 3.Marshall McLuhan in *The Pump House Gang* 4.G.M. Trevelyan in *English Social History* 5.Simone de Beauvoir in *The Second Sex* 6.A.P. Herbert in *Uncommon Law* 7.Lady Bracknell in *The Importance of being Earnest* by Oscar Wilde 8.Glendower in *Henry IV Part I* by William Shakespeare 9.The Warden's in the novel of that name by Anthony Trollope 10.Jeeves's, in the novels of P.G. Wodehouse

WIT AND WISECRACKS

1.Oscar Wilde in *Lady Windermere's Fan* 2.Noel Coward, by Kenneth Tynan in *The Sound of Two Hands Clapping* 3.Dorothy Parker in *Paris Review* 4.P.G. Wodehouse in *The Code of the Woosters* 5.Groucho Marx 6.Robert Morley 7.George Mikes in *English Humour for Beginners* 8.W.S. Gilbert 9.Evelyn Waugh 10.Edna Ferber

☐	99508 8	FIREDRAKE'S EYE	Patricia Finney	£5.99
☐	99479 0	PERFUME FROM PROVENCE	Lady Fortescue	£5.99*
☐	99557 6	SUNSET HOUSE	Lady Fortescue	£5.99*
☐	99558 4	THERE'S ROSEMARY, THERE'S RUE	Lady Fortescue	£5.99*
☐	99488 X	SUGAR CAGE	Connie May Fowler	£5.99
☐	99438 3	A PLACE FOR US	Nicholas Gage	£5.99*
☐	99466 9	A SMOKING DOT IN THE DISTANCE	Ivor Gould	£6.99
☐	12555 5	IN SEARCH OF SCHRÖDINGER'S CAT	John Gribbin	£5.99*
☐	99423 5	BLINDED BY THE LIGHT	John Gribbin	£5.99*
☐	99462 6	IN SEARCH OF THE EDGE OF TIME	John Gribbin	£5.99*
☐	99575 4	IN SEARCH OF THE DOUBLE HELIX	John Gribbin	£6.99*
☐	99443 X	COSMIC COINCIDENCES	John Gribbin & M. Rees	£5.99*
☐	99467 7	MONSIEUR DE BRILLANCOURT	Clare Harkness	£4.99
☐	99387 5	TIME OF GRACE	Clare Harkness	£4.99
☐	99487 1	JIZZ	John Hart	£5.99
☐	99169 4	GOD KNOWS	Joseph Heller	£6.99
☐	99195 3	CATCH-22	Joseph Heller	£6.99
☐	99409 X	SOMETHING HAPPENED	Joseph Heller	£5.99
☐	99538 X	GOOD AS GOLD	Joseph Heller	£6.99
☐	99447 2	MAMMY'S BOY	Domini Highsmith	£5.99
☐	99202 X	LUCIA IN WARTIME	Tom Holt	£5.99
☐	99208 9	THE 158LB MARRIAGE	John Irving	£5.99
☐	99204 6	THE CIDER HOUSE RULES	John Irving	£6.99
☐	99209 7	THE HOTEL NEW HAMPSHIRE	John Irving	£5.99
☐	99369 7	A PRAYER FOR OWEN MEANY	John Irving	£6.99
☐	99206 2	SETTING FREE THE BEARS	John Irving	£5.99
☐	99207 0	THE WATER-METHOD MAN	John Irving	£5.99
☐	99205 4	THE WORLD ACCORDING TO GARP	John Irving	£6.99
☐	99364 6	VIDEO NIGHT IN KATHMANDU	Pico Iyer	£5.99*
☐	99507 X	THE LADY AND THE MONK	Pico Iyer	£5.99*
☐	99141 4	PEEPING TOM	Howard Jacobson	£5.99
☐	99252 6	REDBACK	Howard Jacobson	£5.99
☐	99567 3	SAILOR SONG	Ken Kesey	£6.99
☐	99505 3	TRUTH TO TELL	Ludovic Kennedy	£7.99*
☐	99037 X	BEING THERE	Jerzy Kosinski	£3.99
☐	99384 0	TALES OF THE CITY	Armistead Maupin	£4.99
☐	99086 8	MORE TALES OF THE CITY	Armistead Maupin	£5.99
☐	99106 6	FURTHER TALES OF THE CITY	Armistead Maupin	£5.99
☐	99239 9	BABYCAKES	Armistead Maupin	£5.99
☐	99383 2	SIGNIFICANT OTHERS	Armistead Maupin	£5.99
☐	99374 3	SURE OF YOU	Armistead Maupin	£4.99
☐	99449 9	DISAPPEARING ACTS	Terry McMillan	£5.99
☐	99480 4	MAMA	Terry McMillan	£5.99
☐	99408 1	THE COVER ARTIST	Paul Micou	£4.99
☐	99381 6	THE MUSIC PROGRAMME	Paul Micou	£4.99
☐	99461 8	THE DEATH OF DAVID DEBRIZZI	Paul Micou	£5.99
☐	99501 0	ROTTEN TIMES	Paul Micou	£5.99
☐	99481 2	SIDE BY SIDE	Isabel Miller	£4.99
☐	99504 5	LILA	Robert Pirsig	£5.99
☐	99551 7	SUFFER THE LITTLE CHILDREN	Lucy Robertson	£5.99
☐	99483 9	ZIG ZAG	Lucy Robertson	£4.99

*Non-fiction